An
ILLUSTRATED
Guide To
GHOSTS
& Mysterious Occurrences
in
The Old North State

An
ILLUSTRATED
Guide To
GHOSTS
& Mysterious Occurrences
in
The Old North State

including

THIS
HAUNTED
LAND

Ghosts of the Carolinas

NANCY ROBERTS

PHOTOGRAPHS BY
BRUCE ROBERTS

Castle Books/New Jersey

An Illustrated Guide to Ghosts

© Copyright 1959, 1967 by Nancy Roberts

Library of Congress Catalog Card Number: 59-14157

Manufactured in the United States of America

SECOND EDITION

Thirteenth Printing, 1974

This Haunted Land

© Copyright 1970 by Nancy Roberts and Bruce Roberts
Library of Congress Catalog Card Number: 74–121917

Fourth Printing, 1975

Ghosts of the Carolinas

© Copyright 1962, 1967 by Nancy Roberts

Library of Congress Catalog Card Number 62-21045

Printed in the United States of America

SECOND EDITION

Eleventh Printing, 1974

ARRANGEMENT HAS BEEN MADE TO
PUBLISH THIS EDITION BY CASTLE BOOKS,
A DIVISION OF BOOK SALES, INC.
OF SECAUCUS, N.J.

Manufactured in the United States of America

CONTENTS

PROLOGUE

IN THIS MECHANIZED DAY of television, jet planes and push button kitchens, it has become increasingly difficult for even the most enterprising ghost to find a home.

Haunted houses are ruthlessly torn down to make way for business places and housing developments. American ghosts are disappearing like the buffalo as their haunts give way to progress.

A book of this kind is much harder to put together today than it would have been, say twenty years ago. Even at that time there were quite a few people around who were acquainted with a ghost or two. And ghost stories in those days were the equivalent of TV westerns for the youngsters.

One of the last people who was really a connoisseur of good ghost stories was H. V. Rose of Smithfield. For many years Mr. Rose was Clerk of Court at Smithfield and he spent much of his spare time delving into the history and records of his section of the state.

Before his death last spring, he was kind enough to tell me two of the many stories he had collected. It is with the deepest appreciation that I acknowledge my debt to him for the "Battle of the Dead" and "The Thing at the Bridge." The story of the "Battle of the Dead" had been told to him by Jim Weaver, an eye witness.

There are numerous other older citizens in the towns where these stories took place whose help was invaluable in compiling this collection.

Grateful mention should also be made of the prompt appearance of Joe Baldwin at Maco Station on the stormy October night when I journeyed to see him. He didn't mind being photographed at all . . . or rather his light put up no objections.

Joe, by the way, is one of the few ghosts who have stood their ground against the pressures of civilization. Perhaps this was due to Joe's familiarity with the railroad — for mechanical things have not really upset him.

I was very sorry that the ghost who slammed the door in Hendersonville each night at midnight was not available. He had been living in the "House of the Opening Door," a very respectable ghost house south of town, but unfortunately the house was torn down. I understand from some of my ghost friends that the poor chap is having an unearthly time making a go of it until he can find new haunts.

Tom Fesperman of the *Charlotte Observer*, who I'm sure believes in ghosts, also deserves a word of appreciation. It was due to his interest in our supernatural friends that these stories were published as a series in his paper. That, incidentally, led to this book.

Gratitude is also due Mrs. C. W. Roberts of Winter Park, Florida, for supplying the line drawings in this collection.

I can only hope that some dedicated historical organization will busy itself with the preservation of the haunts of this neglected minority group. They are in grave danger of vanishing before the bulldozer of progress.

NANCY ROBERTS

Charlotte, N. C.
July 15, 1959

PROLOGUE

We believe there are spirits who walk this land and we would like to introduce some of them to you as you read this book.

They are the spirits of the people, both good and bad, who forded the rivers, climbed the hills and cultivated the fields which are our inheritance —men and women who loved and fought and gave the land we call "home" names like Gold Hill, Kings Mountain and Wizard Clip.

Housing developments now cover the countryside where hundreds of miners, many from foreign lands, once worked in the Carolina gold fields. Modern highways slash through hills where King George's men stood in resplendent battle lines. But the builders and developers have only destroyed the physical appearance of the area. They can never kill the ghosts and spirits which must rise at night as surely as does the full moon.

And the supernatural is far from remote. It is a matter of daily experience for those who look for more than mediums and witchcraft can ever offer.

C. S. Lewis once said, "There is no neutral ground in the universe. Every square inch, every split second, is claimed by God and counterclaimed by Satan." The spirits in this book have fought for both sides and there are others who don't appear to have been on any particular side, but dazed by death and perchance in some sort of limbo, they still return to the land they knew in life.

The ghosts in these pages have an attachment for certain places and when you read these stories, we hope you will understand why. For they do not respect the deed books at the county court house. This is THEIR land and they plan to be here through countless centuries, if they so choose. For a time we feared that progress would eliminate spirits but now that we know them better, we become more convinced that the spirits will not only endure, but will outlast "progress."

Bruce and Nancy Roberts
February 4, 1971

P.S. For those who don't believe in ghosts we have a remedy. The first night of the full moon in October walk to the top of Kings Mountain and then down the path to Colonel Ferguson's grave. Spend the next night watching the Brown Mountain lights alone from a deserted overlook on the Blue Ridge Parkway. And, on the third night go alone at midnight to the Devil's Tramping Ground near Siler City and wait for the moon to set. This will help restore your faith.

FOREWORD

MILLIONS OF WORDS have been spoken and written —and effectively—in heralding the attractions and advantages of the Carolinas.

Most of this material has emphasized the physical assets of the region. Some of it has even listed the high spirits of Carolinians as important intangibles in the enumeration of assets.

These promoters of the Carolinas have given little appreciation, as far as I have observed, however, to the virtues of the most intangible of these intangibles, the spirits themselves.

Yet surely no section of the nation can rightfully claim more mystifying, more intriguing, more sadly accusing, more altruistic, or more enduring ghosts. Of a certainty we have our share of the finest shades in all America. And they have gone too long un-catalogued and unappreciated.

But this failure of our generally alert and enter-prising public relations folk to exploit adequately the Carolinas' apparitions has been remedied in part at least by Nancy Roberts and her photographer husband Bruce. With the publication a few years ago of *An Illustrated Guide to Ghosts and Myste-rious Occurrences in the Old North State* and now this volume on other ghosts of both Carolinas, Nancy and Bruce Roberts promulgate our claim to posses-sion of some of the most frightening and charming and authenticated ghosts that have ever walked— or drifted or floated, or, tritely, haunted—the American scene.

The new book evenly shares between the two states certain of the more notable apparitions. Many of these shades even yet materialize, or seem to, from out of the deep past; they are venerable and respected and long have been spoken of even with affection. One such is the Gray Man of Pawley's Island, South Carolina, a benevolent ancient-young man whose appearance to those who see his appari-tion strolling along the beach has become a warning to flee from a closely approaching hurricane. Some are peculiarly and identifiably Carolinian; others are reported to materialize from time to time in widely separated states. Some are not even human emana-tions, like the ghostly Hound of Goshen, a frighten-ing apparition that has scared the daylights out of many persons through long years. But to give that old spirit dog his due, though he has chased dozens, maybe scores or hundreds of horses, mules and terrified people to near exhaustion, he has not to this day bitten man or beast.

Difficult to classify are some of the others in this book—the Brown Mountain lights, for example. Are they the spectral torches of Indian braves slain in a long-ago battle along the mountain's ridges? Or could they be the luminous apparitions of Indian maidens seeking lovers lost in that battle? Or indeed, are they but a natural phenomenon never satis-factorily explained? There are those who think that —persons who, perish the thought, have neither eyes to see a ghost materialize nor ears to hear his almost soundless coming, nor skin sensitized to notice the sudden swift clamminess of his passing. But for a fact the lights do appear above Brown Mountain, whether ghostly, gaseous, reflected, or mirage. I have seen them myself.

To illustrate his wife's intriguing stories, Bruce Roberts has artfully planned and skillfully executed photographs of the sites of certain mysterious oc-currences. And even though they may not convince all the book's readers of the reality of its spectral characters, most surely they must earn the plaudits of the more vainglorious in his ghostly gallery.

LEGETTE BLYTHE

Huntersville, North Carolina
September, 1962

The GENERAL'S *G*HOST

Upon a windswept sandy rampart the ghost of one of the South's great generals still haunts the battlefield

South of Wilmington there is a peninsula of land between the Cape Fear River and the Atlantic Ocean. The distance between the river and the ocean gradually narrows, and near the tip of the land where the highway ends are the remains of Fort Fisher.

This is a haunted land. Mounds of sand with live oak trees twisting among them mark what once was the "Gibraltar of the Confederacy." On one side is the ocean and just beyond the breakers. Sometimes at low tide the skeletons of blockade runners can be seen. There should be many ghosts here. The ghost of the Confederacy is one, for in a sense what happened here made it die. Moreover, there should be the ghosts of hundreds of men who fought and died in one of the most savage hand-to-hand battles ever waged on this continent.

But the ghost seen here is that of a Confederate general, one of the best the Confederacy had.

He was William Whiting, born in Mississippi, graduated first in his class at West Point and former commander of a division of the Army of Northern Virginia.

Several years following the end of the War, a group of Confederate veterans who had served at Fort Fisher returned to visit the wrecked fort. They lingered longer than they had planned, recalling memories of the great battle and still blaming General Bragg for not coming to their aid. As the shadows stretched across the parapets they were startled to see the figure of a Confederate officer climbing to a gun emplacement on the land side of the fort where the old Wilmington road wandered through the trees to the fort entrance.

For a moment they thought another veteran had come to join them although they weren't expecting an officer dressed in Confederate uniform. They watched spellbound as the officer

11

mounted the parapet, gazed in the direction of the old road and then, as they started toward him, vanished.

Each one of the half dozen men knew what the others were thinking. It was the ghost of "Little Billy," as he had been affectionately called by the men who had known him.

For several moments there was silence and then one of the veterans said, "That's the same spot where he was wounded."

Another added, "It's a shame they had to take him to a prison up North to die."

On the trip back to Wilmington nothing else was said.

During the years of Reconstruction other veterans visited the fort. They didn't talk much about the ghost or what they saw there, but this is not uncommon with men after a war is over.

Today, if you go to Fort Fisher and you don't see the General in gray, it is not because he isn't there. If the wind is blowing in from the sea and the breakers are crashing over the timbers of the wrecked ships, you may not hear his footsteps. But wait until dusk and in the shadows of the fort you will sense he is nearby.

Let me tell you what happened there. All through the war Wilmington had been the favorite port for the blockade runners bringing in the supplies which the Confederacy so desperately needed and carrying cotton back to England to get the hard cash to hold the southern economy intact.

But as the war went on, the other ports of the Confederacy were closed one by one, either through capture by Union forces or the growing strength of the Union fleet. By the end of 1864 Wilmington was the only port left open between the Confederacy and the outside world, and it was protected by the "Gibraltar of the South," Fort Fisher.

The fort had been built out of sand, marsh grass, pine timbers and the imagination and skill of its commanding officer, Colonel William Lamb. Colonel Lamb took command of the fort on July 4, 1862, when it "amounted to nothing" and two years later had a fort of such strength that the Union fleet dared not come too close to the entrance of the river. Happy were the blockade runners when they came within range of the fort's guns, for the pursuing Yankee ships were then forced to turn back.

Fort Fisher became such a problem for the Union that President Lincoln, pacing the corridors of the White House in Washington, finally made the ultimate decision—to send practically the entire Atlantic fleet and the best of his troops against it.

In December of '64 General Lee's aides brought word that the Union was gathering a great armada of ships to attack Fort Fisher. General Lee had written that so long as the port of Wilmington remained open his army had a chance. But Lee knew Colonel Lamb and his 36th North Carolina regiment stationed at the fort were no match for the force the Union was about to hurl against them.

Despite Lee's own shortage of troops, he immediately dispatched General Robert F. Hoke and six thousand of his veteran troops to Fort Fisher. These troops would be placed under the general commanding the Department of Wilmington, which roughly embraced all the Confederate defenses along the river.

Unfortunately Jefferson Davis, the Confederate president, chose this moment to send one of his favorite generals to take command of the area from General Whiting. Sentiment in the South was summed up by one line in a Richmond newspaper which said: "Bragg has been sent to command the troops at Wilmington—good-bye Wilmington."

The Union commander of the invasion fleet was also most unpopular in the South. General Benjamin Butler, called "Beast" Butler, landed his troops a few miles up the beach out of range of the guns of the fort. It was his plan after the mass shelling by the Union fleet to then move his troops in and take the fort.

While the Union gunboats blazed incessantly at the fort, a young Confederate fell into the hands of Butler's pickets. The captured soldier casually mentioned that Hoke and his men were on their way to save the fort. Upon hearing this news, General Butler quickly surveyed the fort and decided his position was precarious. He immediately ordered a retreat back to the beach. Butler may not have been the first man off the beach but he was certainly not the last. His army left in such haste that they forgot an entire brigade, leaving it on the beach for the night.

In the morning, through the efforts of the navy, the brigade was rescued and Butler and his fleet returned North in humiliation.

General Bragg had staged an elaborate review of Hoke's troops for the citizens of Wilmington and then had ordered Hoke's men to "dig in" at a place called Sugar Loaf about eight miles up the peninsula. Bragg himself set up his headquarters at Sugar Loaf with Hoke and his men, several batteries of artillery and about 1,500 North Carolina Reserves.

After the first attack on the fort failed, General Bragg congratulated both Whiting and Lamb for their successful defense. However, these same officers were not lulled into apathy by the praise of the commanding general. They appealed for more guns, men and ammunition. Lamb and

Whiting knew the Federals would be back with more men and ships for another try. General Bragg did not agree.

Lincoln replaced Butler with a competent general and on January 12, 1865, Colonel Lamb mounted the ramparts of his fort and saw "the most formidable fleet that ever floated on the sea" supplemented by transports carrying 8,500 men. This time the fleet began an immediate and intense bombardment of the fort which in the Colonel's words was "beyond description." The bombardment continued day and night. The Confederates, short of gunpowder and shells, were ordered by Lamb to fire each gun only once every half hour.

When it became apparent to Whiting that Bragg was not going to strongly reinforce the fort but remain at Sugar Loaf with his Army, General Whiting commandeered a ship and sailed down the river to Fort Fisher alone. Walking through the bursting shells he entered the fort and found Colonel Lamb at his post. Above the roar of the guns he shouted to the Colonel, "Lamb, my boy, I have come to share your fate. You and your garrison are to be sacrificed."

Lamb could not believe Bragg would desert him and asked, "Where are Hoke's men?" Whiting replied that when he left Headquarters, General Bragg had just issued orders for removing his stores and ammunition and was "looking for a place to fall back upon."

The Federal troops poured ashore on the beach far enough north to be out of range of the fort's guns. As the blue regiments formed and began their advance Whiting telegraphed an urgent message to Bragg:

"The enemy are about to assault; they outnumber us heavily. We are just manning our parapets. Fleet has extended down the sea front outside and firing heavily. Enemy on the beach in front of us in very heavy force, not more than 700 yards from us. Nearly all land guns disabled. Attack! Attack! It is all I can say and all you can do."

In response to this appeal Bragg dispatched what he said was "eleven hundred veteran infantry" down the river by steamer. The ships were fired upon heavily by the Federal guns and less than half the men reached the fort. Colonel Lamb put the figure at 350 South Carolinians of Johnson Hagood's brigade. Unfortunately, the troops had to run a half-mile under the naval bombardment from the Union guns. They reached the fort out of breath and Colonel Lamb immediately sent them to an old bomb shelter to rest. This was the last help Lamb was to receive.

All at once the great Union fleet stopped firing and blew their steam whistles. It was the signal for the final attack. At the point where the land and sea faces of the fort joined facing the beach, several thousand Union marines and sailors charged. Lamb with a few hundred of his men threw them back in a fierce hand-to-hand fight. Just as it appeared this attack was over, three Federal battle flags appeared on the ramparts of the fort to the west. Eight thousand Federal troops followed these flags.

Both Whiting and Lamb gathered what men were left and launched a counterattack. The fighting swirled from gun emplacement to gun emplacement. In the smoke and roar of battle a Union officer shouted to Whiting to surrender. "Go to hell!" Whiting replied. A moment later he sank to the sand mortally wounded. Colonel Lamb, fighting on with a few hundred of his men, was also wounded and the command fell to Major James Reilly, who made the final stand at the last gun emplacement.

General Whiting was taken prisoner and, despite his wounds, was taken to a Union prison on Governor's Island in New York harbor where he died a short time later.

The spot where Whiting fell in the battle is unmarked. The area now is part of a state historic site. It has been some time since the gray-clad figure of the Confederate general has been seen, but go to Fort Fisher at dusk and listen to the wind and the waves if you would doubt that his spirit still lingers there.

The UNEARTHLY MUSIC
of ROAN MOUNTAIN

Go to the top if you would hear its awesome sound

O nce upon a time there was a man who had all of the things most men spend themselves for.

First of all he could number among his list of acquaintances many of the most famous men of his day. Why, at any moment, even here in the fashionable seclusion of his mountain home, the phone might ring. And the voice of a publisher, politician or other prominent friend would come warmly over the wires seeking him out.

A writer such as he had much to contribute, especially now that his position in the literary world was secure. His most prosaic utterances were received as conversational gems. Even his physical presence was a contribution in the eyes of many. For certainly such a distinguished guest enhanced his host's prestige. And unsure of personal worth, how much better to huddle close to those who have arrived.

Lamotte Duval, and we will call him that to save possible embarrassment, had been everywhere. Just a casual reference to the countries he had visited was bound to impress. It had all been most exciting until he began to notice that hungry children were the same whether they begged on the streets of India or sat apathetically on the steps of a sharecropper's house and that the stench of

poverty was as strong in the New York slums as in those of Morocco.

The time he had sought the most avaricious face to describe which he could find, the man he had found was not among the gamblers at Monte Carlo—but among his own circle in the exclusive apartment house where he spent most of his winters.

A vague dissatisfaction, the cause of which he could scarcely come to grips with, had become Duval's most frequent companion of late. He sat now in a comfortable chair facing a huge expanse of plate glass which overlooked one of the most gorgeous views in the North Carolina mountains.

In some towns standing might depend on a grandfather, an address at the top of the hill, or a certain street name. But here one of the most important symbols of status was "the view." And, of course, Lamotte Duval had it. In fact, what did he not have? On his magazine table were expensive and exquisitely done publications—a tribute to his taste. His bookshelves were lined with rare incunabulas and first editions.

And now he was faced with deciding how and where he was to spend his summer. Should it be here in the mountains or would he really prefer listening to Wagner in Bayreuth, with an apart-

15

ment for the summer at the Kronberg Castle near Frankfurt and perhaps a jaunt to the Olympic games.

Ten years ago he might have savoured all this to the utmost. But ever so gradually a serpent had insinuated itself into this paradise and all but ruined his capacity to enjoy it. And just what was this viper? He didn't know himself. Ah, if it had been a man of more talent, superior intellect whose work rivalled his own, he could have adjusted to that. For he had come to accept, nay even to thoroughly appreciate the genius of other men.

Long years ago he had renounced that illusory and prideful struggle for recognition by the world as the "best" writer. Duval had been content to work diligently developing his own unique talent while tasting the not inconsiderable fruits of his labors.

But now an honest and incisive mind had finally turned itself inward. And the picture which Duval was beginning to see of himself and his life was not altogether pleasing. Although he had regarded religion with amused tolerance for the greatest part of his life, it now began to appear to him that this "myth of the masses" which he had failed to pursue had somehow begun to pursue him.

If he casually fingered a book it would turn out to be by Fenelon or perhaps Thomas à Kempis. And often it seemed that even the most impersonally begun conversation would turn toward religion. But the phenomena in the book of mountain stories he was now reading were clearly of scientific origin. As long as he was here so close to the locale he owed it to himself to investigate.

"The ghostly choir of Roan Mountain" some of the natives called it. Roan Mountain was not a long drive, and Lamotte read with fascination that on this mile-high plateau an awesome sound like wildly beautiful music had first been heard

by herdsmen. This was as far back as the 1770's. When they told the story in the valley they spoke of hearing "a choir of angels."

As they talked the heads of the mountain folk nodded, for hadn't some venturesome souls been caught on the Roan in a thunderstorm and seen a circular rainbow. And if God wore a halo would it not be just such a rainbow? Anything could happen atop the Roan.

Here Lamotte Duval smiled at such naivety. For he had been to many faraway lands but never in any of them had he seen even one magic place. And yet at the thought of magic places some long-buried emotion of his youth stirred faintly within him. He read on about John Strother, member of a boundary surveying commission back in 1799. In his diary Strother had written:

"There is no shrubbery growing on the top of this mountain for several miles, and the wind has such power on top of this mountain that the ground is blowed in deep holes all over the northwest side."

And then in 1878 Colonel John Wilder heard the music as it had been heard a century before by the herdsmen. He built a summer hotel on the Roan and passed the story along to many an interested guest.

Among those who heard of it was a young scientist from Knoxville, Tennessee, named Henry E. Colton. Colton returned home to publish a treatise. Lamotte Duval read Colton's conclusions avidly.

"Several of the cattle tenders on the mountain and also Colonel Wilder had spoken to us about what they called 'Mountain Music,'" Colton wrote. "One evening they said it was sounding loud and Dr. D. P. Boynton of Knoxville, Hon. J. M. Thornburg and myself accompanied General Wilder to the glen to hear it. The sound was very plain to the ear. It was always loudest and most prolonged just after there would be a thunderstorm in either valley or one passing over the mountain. I used every argument I could to persuade myself that it simply was a result of some common cause and to shake the faith of the country people in its mysterious origin." They continued believing that the music came from angels. "But I only convinced myself that it was the result from two currents of air meeting each other in the suck between the two peaks where there was no obstruction of trees, one containing a greater, the other a lesser amount of electricity."

Here Lamotte Duval put down the book with sudden decision. This very afternoon he would learn the truth for himself. He noted the black clouds overhead. An occasional raindrop made a shiny little path as it slid down the outside of the wall of glass before him. Without waiting for his resolve to waver he strode out of the house and, getting into his small, foreign-make car, headed toward Roan Mountain.

When he reached the mountain he drove almost to its top, parked his car and began walking toward the crest of the plateau. In a few minutes he saw a line of rocks which he guessed to be where the foundation of Colonel John Wilder's hotel had been. By now the rain was a steady downpour beating against his face with almost primeval force. Stumbling, he caught himself at the edge of a rocky promontory and decided to take shelter under its overhanging edge.

For almost a half hour he sat there waiting for the rain to stop, soaked to the skin. As he rested he began to berate himself for his foolishness, for there was certainly no music of any kind to be heard—only the pounding of the torrential rain.

Then as he strained to hear the slightest unusual noise his ears caught a faint sound. The rain stopped as if at the signal of some unseen hand and the sun drifted brilliantly from behind a cloud. Then he heard the sound again and more clearly. Gradually it gained in intensity, and what

had first seemed to him to be merely the wind took on new tones like a choir of many voices. Wildly sweet, it built up to a shattering crescendo of sound which caught him up and flowed over him.

He listened incredulously, forgetting his damp discomfort. As he did so something indescribable began to take place within Lamotte Duval. Oriental women of old bound their feet, and so had the world placed fetter after fetter around Duval's spirit. Now it seemed as if one by one they were being unwound and swept away.

Finally all was quiet and Lamotte Duval, emotionally exhausted and utterly bewildered by the fierce beauty of the music, still made no move to rise. Then he climbed cautiously back upon the rocks above him. His eyes searched the sky for more storm clouds. They had completely disappeared, but to his astonishment there was something else in their place.

At the south edge of the plateau was the most gorgeous rainbow he had ever beheld. Blue, yellow, pale green and cerise, it shimmered high in the sky. And what was most amazing of all, the rainbow formed a complete circle! He remembered the words "God's halo," and as he did so his lips tried to form a smile. But they could not.

He clutched desperately at the last shreds of his skepticism. But they melted away. As he stood there gazing in wonderment he began to be aware of a new sensation. Somehow he felt as new and clean as he had as a boy. Duval watched the rainbow's glory until it faded into the sky and then, turning reluctantly, started back to his car.

When he reached home he was just in time to hear the insistent ring—ring—ring of his phone. But it could as easily have been ringing in another world on another planet. For Lamotte Duval smiled faintly and, heeding it not at all, walked over to his table by the window.

The book which he picked up and opened was just what he had thought it would be—"The Imitation of Christ" by Thomas à Kempis.

The girl in the fog hailed the oncoming car.

The Lovely Apparition

Beautiful Lydia haunts the highway pleading for help, and no mortal man can help her . . . though many have tried

There are few men who do not hold within them some experience which time cannot erase. For some men that experience is a woman. And for Burke Hardison it will always be Lydia.

Nor is he the only man who has encountered her. Since 1923 this young lady has appeared from time to time at her favorite spot. Men who have tried to help her have all told the same story afterwards. The story has been one of complete bafflement and mystery.

Burke Hardison met Lydia late one rainy night in the early spring of 1924. He was on his way back from Raleigh to his home in High Point. The evening had been spent with friends made during his college years at State. And it must have been almost two o'clock as he neared the little community of Jamestown.

All around him the countryside slumbered under a billowing blanket of fog. Even the most obvious landmarks had silently vanished and there was an air of unreality about the misty world through which he drove. Along with this air of unreality came the feeling that all other life had ceased to exist save himself.

For miles there had been no other cars, but his eyes still strained as he peered through the mist for tail lights ahead. In front of him loomed the Highway 70 underpass. For a moment the fog seemed to clear. He was no longer alone. At the mouth of the underpass stood the slight, graceful figure of a girl. Dressed in a white evening gown, her arm was flung upward signalling desperately for him to stop.

Even before he pulled to the side of the road, he knew she must be in some terrible distress. He opened the door of the car as she came toward him.

"Please, will you help me get to High Point?" pleaded a soft, tear-laden voice.

"I'm on my way there now, and I'll be glad to help you," replied Burke. A gust of fog entered the car as the girl slid in beside him. He could see the pale blur of a lovely face surrounded by a halo of dark hair. And the diaphanous cloud of her white dress rested on the seat.

After she had given him the address of a street he was vaguely familiar with they drove in silence. Nearing High Point he felt that he must

19

find out more about her and began to question
her.

Her name was Lydia and if there was more
than that it faded into the fog. Her words seemed
almost detached and so faint that he could hear
them above the sound of the motor only with
the greatest effort.

She seemed deeply distressed at the late hour
and afraid her mother would be worried about
her. Gradually he gathered that she had been to
a dance that evening in Raleigh. But what had
happened and how she came to be standing alone
in the fog at the underpass, she either could not
or would not tell him.

At times she failed to answer him at all.

"Why do you question me?" she finally asked.
"Nothing is important now, but that I'm going
home."

So nothing more was said. He found the street
she had given him and there stood the house on
the corner just as she had described it. Well, he
would not bother her further.

Opening his door, he got out and walked
around to the other side of the car. Then he held
the door open for his young passenger. But as
he stared into the blackness of the car's interior
he gasped in amazement.

The car was empty—his companion gone.

Nor was there a sign of any living being near
it. The only movement was that of the fog as it
swirled in front of his headlights. For a moment
he stood as if dazed, with his hand still on the
door. Then such a cold chill swept over him that
he slammed the car door to and pulled his coat
close around him.

Perhaps she had slipped into the house without
his seeing her. He knew that he must find out.
It was several minutes before his knock was
answered and then it was not Lydia who opened
the door. But the resemblance was there in the

The house looked eerie in the fog.

face of the old lady who confronted him.

"I'm Burke Hardison and I just brought your
daughter home but she seems to have disappeared.
Is she here?" asked Burke.

For a moment the old lady didn't answer. He
could see the bright shimmer of tears welling
into her eyes behind her glasses and she seemed
to crumple before him.

"Are you trying to play some cruel joke on
me?" said she. His bafflement turned to anger
and he would have answered harshly but the
tragedy in her face was genuine.

He explained how the young girl had stopped
him at the underpass and begged him to take her
home. And then he told how he had arrived at
this address only to open the door of the car and
find she had disappeared.

"I had an only daughter named Lydia," said
the old lady. "A year ago she was killed in a
wreck near the underpass as she was coming
home from a dance." Tears slid helplessly down
her cheeks.

"This is not the first time people have tried
to bring her home. But somehow she never quite
gets here."

Run *of the* Ghost Train

Mrs. Lowry was a little girl when she stepped from the track to let the southbound train go by. She'll never forget what happened then

There is little in the realm of the supernatural which can quite match the fascination of a ghost train. It holds a unique grip on the imagination of men.

An eerie headlight flashing down the track followed by empty, rattling coaches. The wail in the night of a lonely, haunting whistle as it echoes over quiet countryside.

North Carolina ghost lore would not be complete without the story of just such a train.

In the fall of 1906 the tiny lumbering town of Warsaw contained only a few country stores, a small family style hotel, and numerous sawmills.

A short distance from town beside the tracks of the Atlantic Coast Line railroad lived the family of Henry McCauley. Each night when Mrs. McCauley finished her work at the hotel her family would meet her and together they would walk home down the railroad tracks.

It was late one November night and the fields around Warsaw lay white with frost. The McCauleys walked along the trestle leading toward their home, talking occasionally in low tones. The only other sound was the crunch of their footsteps on the stones between the ties.

Suddenly the sharp whistle of an approaching train pierced the cold autumn air. "Hurry, we're going to have to run to get to our crossing," shouted Henry McCauley to his wife and daughter.

The huge headlight was so close that it seemed the train was almost upon them. They ran panic-stricken across the trestle toward their crossing, gasping in the cold air until their chests hurt. Too winded to talk they reached safety and stood waiting for the train to pass.

There up the track ahead shone the headlight just as bright as before. Again there was the sound of the whistle. They waited and wondered but no noisy, smoke-belching engine hurtled past them out of the darkness. In fact there was nothing—no real train at all.

It was the ghost train again.

The McCauleys weren't the only ones to see the ghost train. Several nights later the train from Norfolk to Wilmington approached Warsaw. The heart of the train's engineer leaped to his throat.

The single track ahead of him was brightly illuminated by the headlight of an approaching train. A train where no train should ever have been. He reached for his brake and there was the sound of wheels screeching in the night. Even before he had brought his train to a stop trainmen jumped off and started up the tracks to investigate.

But they soon returned shaking their heads and with nothing to report. As far as anyone could tell there was no train there! A puzzled engineer and his crew went on their way. From that night on they would slow as they reached the spot but they didn't stop again.

What was the reason for the ghost train?

The ghost train started making its eerie run after a tragic accident. "I was just a little girl when it happened," says Henry McCauley's daughter, who is now Mrs. Kirk Lowry of York, South Carolina. "It gave me a queer feeling—one that I never want to have again."

Mrs. Lowry's story begins on a crisp November morning of 1906.

"I was walking down the track on the way to my grandmother's one morning when I heard the whistle of the southbound train. The old people called it the 'Shoo Fly.' Why, I don't know, but they always had and I guess they always would.

"I stepped off the track to let the 'Shoo Fly' go by, and I'll never forget what happened then."

At one moment the train was chugging down the track toward the child who stood watching. The next moment there was a horrible wrenching sound and the monstrous, black engine twisted to one side as if in agony. Then, still emitting huge puffs of steam, it careened wildly off the track and turned completely over. Behind it the baggage car gave a mighty lurch and came to a halt leaning crazily at a 45 degree angle.

"The first thing I remember after that was a

man's voice screaming for help from the baggage car."

By now passengers were piling out of the Pullman and men were trying to dig their way through tons of baggage to reach the buried baggage master. He died of a broken back before they could get to him.

In the cab of the engine all was quiet.

The engineer and the fireman never answered the shouts of those who sought to rescue them. They had both been scalded to death.

The accident was the strangest kind of freak. The night before the ill-fated "Shoo Fly" went chugging along on its Norfolk to Wilmington run, a northbound freight stopped at the siding.

There was a saw mill next to the track and the freight train picked up one timber-laden car after another. Then the freight train had been moved out of the siding.

As the last flat car went by the main line track switch, a protruding piece of timber hit the switch and opened it. Three men were to die as a result.

By the next morning when the southbound "Shoo Fly" was due, the open switch had still not been discovered. Disaster was inevitable when the train hit the open switch at full speed.

Gilbert Horne, the engineer killed on the "Shoo Fly," had been in railroading since he was a boy. How natural that his son Will should follow in his father's footsteps.

But what a tragic coincidence that the son should be engineer of the freight which had re-opened the switch and caused the death of his father!

The little girl who ran with her parents along the railroad trestle over 50 years ago will never forget the wreck or the ghost train which followed it.

"I saw that light with my own eyes and heard the whistle," she says thoughtfully. "Where the ghost train came from or where it went to, I'll never know. But it went by our house almost every night 'til we moved away."

The Fairy Cross

Season follows season in the mountains of Western North Carolina and some of the more isolated areas seem to have been little changed by the passage of time. Red and gold maples are gradually disrobed by winter winds and the black tracery of their limbs make outlines against the pale winter's sky. Days turn into weeks until once again spring surges through the valleys and slopes leaving tender green leaves and wild flowers in her wake.

There is something in this process which heals the broken hearts of men and so it might one day for John Sebastian and his daughter, Selina. It had now been almost a year since he began his duties as a hired hand for the old couple on their small farm in the North Carolina mountains.

The Sebastians were different from the mountain people and the old man and his wife had been quick to sense it. Although nearly a year had now passed since the arrival of the Sebastians, they had never penetrated the father and daughter's reserve.

Tonight, grateful for the warmth of the fire on the crisp fall night, the four were clustered around the hearth. The inroads which sorrow had made on the face of the father did not escape the old man. Nor did the look of pain in Sebastian's eyes when he saw the old man tenderly place a cushion at his wife's back.

As it began to grow late and only the flickering fire light pushed the darkness back, the faces became a blur to each other. Somehow this made it easier to speak of that which was nearest the heart. The increased intimacy encouraged the old couple to probe in a kindly manner and finally the tide of emotion John Sebastian had long held back, overflowed and he found release and comfort in words.

Almost ten years ago he and his wife Anna with their infant son and six year old daughter had saved enough to go back to Anna's homeland and visit her parents.

It was a joyful reunion for all. The old people saw and adored their grandchildren. He and his wife again attended the village church where they had first met during the gaiety of a religious holiday.

All too soon it was time for them to leave. In the early morning hours of the day of departure, he and his six year old daughter were roughly awakened and seized by the secret police. His own questions and his wife's pleading and tears had no effect, nor were they given any assurance of when they would see each other again. "In a few hours the future lay bleak and shattered around us," said Sebastian.

"All that was left to me was Selina," and he reached toward her covering her hand with his.

"We were put on a train and sent out of the country with warnings not to try to take Ann and my little son back to America."

"In the long years since, I have entreated the authorities of the country to allow them to come to America. Many kind people have tried to help us, but no one has yet succeeded."

When he was finished there was a long quiet broken only by the crackling of the fire. The old couple said little knowing through experience the time when words bring slight comfort.

Finally, the old man began to reminisce about the days of his youth and from his experiences during years of real poverty, threaded with humor and love, he went on to talk of the mountains themselves and of the legends surrounding them.

"Have you ever heard of the fairy crosses?" he asked.

"No," said Sebastian. "Would you have me believe in fairies?"

"You must judge that for yourself," replied the old man. "I only know that I have seen fairy crosses with my own eyes although they are very difficult to come upon."

"Years ago when these mountains were young all of the caves and the hollow trees along with the sheltered places in the woods were inhabited by a fairy people. They were a happy, carefree lot laboring little and much given to frolics."

"One night in early spring they were dancing merrily around a mountain pool. The pool is said to be not far from this cabin although I myself have never been able to find it."

"While they were dancing a messenger arrived from the spirit world to tell them that the Son of God had been crucified on a cross. As they listened tears began to fall from their eyes. Each tear falling to the ground formed a tiny but perfect cross."

"On rare occasions one of these crosses is found by men. Among the Cherokee Indians they were believed to possess strange and wondrous powers."

Pulling himself up from the chair with the stiffness of age, the old man said goodnight to

25

Sebastian and his daughter. Sebastian decided to fold several blankets in a sort of pallet and lay down to look into the fire. There was a self-forgetful fascination in staring at the flames and soon he found himself dozing off. Several hours later Sebastian awakened and his thoughts turned to the alternating despair and hope with which he had lived for so long. He got up and opened the door of the cabin.

The faint flush of dawn was just beginning to appear along the tops of the mountains. He decided to go out and walk for awhile alone. His daughter and the old man and his wife were sleeping soundly.

Lost in his thoughts he took first one trail and then another. With each turn he continued to climb upward until he found himself on a steep, rocky path leading into a little clearing. Here he decided to rest. Leaning back against a rock, he gazed out across ridge after ridge of purplish blue mountains, their peaks just emerging from diaphanous layers of clouds. It was a breathtakingly beautiful sight. But his climb had thoroughly exhausted him and he fell asleep.

Once again, he heard the clear, sweet tones of bells. He was with his wife, Anna. It was a bright, sunlit day and they were on their way to the small village church to celebrate the holiday. He saw her face—the dark hair growing back so smoothly from the temples and the deepset, smoky blue eyes—as she walked beside him. His little boy's fingers were clasped tightly around his own.

After a time, John Sebastian became aware of the rocky, uneven ground beneath his body. He opened his eyes on the brilliant October morning and at first thought he must have awakened in the palace of some Midas of old. The glowing colors of the fall foliage surrounded him. A small animal scurried through the underbrush near him and for the first time he was conscious of the rocky ground and the cramped position of the arm on which he had rested his head. He realized his hand was clenched tightly around a tiny object. Relaxing his fingers he looked curiously at the little brown piece of stone in his grasp.

To his surprise he found that it was a tiny but perfect cross. He had never seen anything like it before. Certainly, he had not had it when he had fallen asleep heartsick and exhausted. He recalled the story the old man had told him before—the story of the fairy crosses and their miraculous powers. This diminutive but perfectly formed cross could only be one of the fairy crosses. Sebastian looked at it long and wonderingly.

Still holding it tightly in his hand he began to descend the path and find his way back toward the cabin where he knew his daughter must long have been awake and wondering at his absence.

It was not until he was perhaps halfway down the mountain that he became gloriously aware of something. There was a difference in the very heart of his being. The weight within him which he had carried up the mountain during those early dawn hours was miraculously gone. In place of the pain which had wrapped itself tightly about his heart for so long, there was a sense of joy and peace.

Nearing the end of the trail which led to the cabin, he saw his daughter running toward him. Tears streamed down her face and for a moment it seemed that his heart would stop beating. But as she reached him he saw that they were tears of happiness.

"Mother and Jan are coming to us—at last! The news came just a few minutes ago. They will finally allow them to leave."

John Sebastian held his daughter close and said nothing. For what did he need to say and what did he need to know. He felt the pressure of the fairy cross in his hand and he knew that he would believe the legend forever. Believe that somehow his own tears and those of the fairies had been seen and blessed by the One for whom the fairies' tears were shed.

Music by the Ghost Organ

To this day no one can explain why the organ played at old Kadesh Church

A carpenter of sorts, Horatio Carter was a rolling stone. He would not have had it any other way. He liked to meander from town to town, stopping for a few months wherever the mood struck him.

Since late summer he had been making his home in the small community of Kadesh in the rolling green hills of upper Cleveland county.

On this particular October afternoon shortly after the close of World War I, he could have

27

been seen walking up the hill from which Kadesh Methodist Church surveyed the surrounding farms. A battered straw hat shielded Horatio from the hot autumn sun and under his arm was a satchel containing his carpentry tools.

As he walked he hummed a snatch of the "Muskrat Ramble" and with more humor than sorrow meditated on the quirks of a fate which had kept him poor.

Entering the front door of the old church he found the window with the rotted sill and set about his task of replacing it. He had been at work for possibly half an hour when he heard footsteps at the rear of the church.

There was the sound of a chair scraping on the wood floor. And then the bellows of the organ emitted an introductory wheeze. In a few seconds the church was filled with music. But it was music the like of which Horatio had never heard before. It was neither hymn nor ballad. Nor did it resemble the minstrel tunes of which Horatio was so fond.

It was like the soft rustle of the night wind through the trees or the melodious pleading of a harp plucked gently by unseen fingers.

Leaving his work, the carpenter walked down the aisle toward the organ. There was an eerie quality about the perfectly blended chords of the unknown melody. As he approached they died softly away, the last notes lingering for a moment in the air about him.

What Horatio saw when he reached the organ was startling indeed. The chair at the organ was empty—the choir loft deserted. With a terrified cry the itinerant carpenter fled, his work forgotten and his tools unclaimed.

Early the following afternoon the minister of Kadesh church knocked at the door of the farmhouse where Horatio boarded. Much to his surprise he found that the carpenter had left that morning.

"That poor fellow was took near crazy," said the good woman who answered the preacher's knock. "All he could say over and over was he wouldn't work no place where organs just went to playing of themselves."

The puzzled minister shook his head in bewilderment. He confided the incident to several of his church officers but they were as much at a loss as he.

"Might be he was helping hisself to some white lightnin' while he wuz workin', preacher," offered one of them, smiling broadly.

It was a night in late November and the biting cold of winter had wrapped its frost white cloak over the fields of the little foothills community. A prominent Kadesh farmer rode hastily to fetch the doctor for his wife in labor. As he approached the church he could have sworn he heard strains of music wafted toward him by the wind. Slowing almost to a stop, he listened.

An unearthly melody was coming clearly from the direction of old Kadesh church. On and on played the weird music emanating from the pitch dark church silhouetted against the moonlit sky. But the frightened farmer had no desire to linger and hear it out.

Word of the mysterious music at Kadesh Church began to spread. Others claimed to have heard it but none stayed to investigate.

One Sunday night services were brought to a halt by the start of a dust storm. After the congregation had gone, the minister finished closing the windows to shut out the fine cloud of dust which was blowing in and beginning to settle everywhere.

Finally, he was ready to leave, but on this night the heart of the Kadesh pastor was heavy. Only a minister comes to know the deep frustrations, guilt and heartbreak of the people he serves. Oftentimes the load can be overwhelming and so it was for the pastor tonight. He decided

28

to sit down alone and read a few passages from his Bible.

So absorbed was he that only gradually did he notice that his thoughts were accompanied by the softest of melodies. Familiar with church music as he was, he could not recall ever having heard anything similar. It floated about him with a strangely haunting quality.

He walked toward the organ feeling that he must see this organist who could play melodies of pervasive sadness with such consummate skill. As he approached, the music grew very soft, then ceased altogether. When he reached the organ he froze with disbelief. For where he had firmly

expected to see some unknown musician, he found himself confronted only by an empty chair.

Nor was there anyone to be found in the choir loft. Its door was bolted just as he had left it. The minister edged forward for a closer look at the organ itself. Over its stained oak top lay a coating of dust. He drew an exploratory finger across the keys. They too were coated with the fine grey film.

And now as he stared at the coating of dust on the keyboard the minister was certain of one thing. No human hands had been responsible for the music in Kadesh Church.

Bummer's End

Fifty corpses swung from the trees in the swamp... and another dangled over two new graves in a quiet family cemetery

30

Near Smithfield in Johnson County is a swamp. A short distance from its shore—almost hidden by mist—lies an island. The sunlight is shut out by trees and matted vines. It is a perfect setting for a ghost.

But no fictional, storybook ghost lurks among the cyprus. Instead, the swamp is haunted by the ghosts of fifty real men—men who died the way they lived.

It was the twilight of the War Between the States. In North Carolina Sherman had cut a devastating path across the state. In his wake came the dregs of war—the bummers.

They were men who belonged to no army. Stragglers and riffraff who plundered and took what they pleased because there was no law, no order, no force left to stop them.

The swamp today is the same as it was that night almost a hundred years ago. A night when scores of trees bore a gruesome burden. Altogether there were almost 50 bodies swaying in the breeze when morning came.

The story of the swamp and that night of vengeance starts at a plantation home near Smithfield.

Colonel John Saunders had returned to his home to recover from a Yankee bayonet thrust in his hip. Late one summer night he and his wife awoke to the sound of a loud banging on the front door.

Saunders painfully made his way toward it. His wife lay in bed listening to the soft dragging sound of her husband's useless leg as he went to the door.

"Who's there?" he called out.

"David Fanning, sir," came the reply. "I have a sick man and am badly in need of shelter for him."

"What division?" asked the Colonel.

"Wheeler's Confederate cavalry," was the answer.

31

Saunders opened the door and as he did so rough hands grabbed him. Pain shot through his hip like liquid fire. Surrounding him in the yard were two dozen hard faced, ragged men on mules.

The man who seemed to be their spokesman was somewhat better dressed than the rest. He wore two revolvers and a cavalry sword swung at his side.

"All we want's a little information," said he.

"Bummers, eh," replied the Colonel contemptuously. "You'll get nothing from me."

"Oh, won't we, old fellow," said the leader impudently. "Show us where you keep your money and jewelry."

Colonel Saunders refused.

"String him up men! Bring out his wife and hang them both from the same tree."

And the bummer struck Saunders brutally across the face.

By daybreak all that remained of the Saunders' home was a huge area of still smouldering timber. Nearby a single pig which had escaped the plunderers rooted in the ashes.

Several weeks later a young officer stood before his commander, General Joseph Wheeler.

"Sir, I would ask permission to hunt down the bummers who murdered my parents," said Saunders, his eyes dark with pain.

"I cannot direct you on a mission of personal revenge," replied Wheeler, "but this I will do.

"Take 20 men into Johnson County and do everything possible to rout bummers wherever you find them. They are important sources of supplies to Union troops in this section. You have my permission to go after them."

Day and night young Saunders and his men sought out bummers, shooting and hanging them as they went. But there was no sign of the group they hoped to find.

They were ready to return when word came that the Rance Massengill plantation had been burned to the ground. Bummers were reportedly camped near the end of Devil's Race Track eight miles below Smithfield.

The bummers must have sensed danger for by the time Saunders and his men arrived they had fled toward Hannah's Creek Swamp.

Excited country people ran from their homes to stop Saunders and his men as they passed. "They're in the swamp. There's an island in the middle with 50 men on it," went the talk.

After some thought, Saunders decided he would lose too many men if he attempted to rush the island. "Go home and come back with all the old clothes you can find," he told the country people.

A few hours later it was dark. Dressed in the old clothes, Saunders and his men set out in boats for the island. The light of their torches cast fiery, dancing images on the black swamp water.

A challenge rang out from the island.

"Who goes there?"

And the men in the boats replied, "Bummers from Harnett County. To hell with the Confederacy!"

They were welcomed with glad shouts. Leaving their rifles stacked in their camp the bummers rushed to the boats to greet their comrades.

Too late they realized that these were no friends. Twenty armed men eyed them with cold relentlessness.

"Who is your leader?" asked Saunders.

"David Fanning, at your service," answered a bold voice and a tall bummer stepped forward.

"My named is John Saunders. Is it familiar?"

Fanning's swaggering manner dropped from him and his face grayed. "Why it must be . . ."

"Yes, I am Colonel Saunders' son," said the young Lieutenant quietly.

"Search each man," ordered Saunders. Forcing the reluctant Fanning to lift his arms, Saunders searched his pockets. Beneath his handkerchief in the pocket of his coat he felt a small object cold to the touch.

As he drew it out a fine gold chain fell to the ground and in his hand lay a gold crucifix—his own Mother's.

"Hang every man of them, but not Fanning," ordered Saunders.

The two waited together as one man after another was strung up. When there were none left and the dark figures of the bummers hung silently in the moonlight Saunders mounted his horse.

With Fanning cowering beside him, they rode to his Father's plantation. Past the blackened ruins toward the family cemetery they rode. Two new headstones shone whitely under the limbs of a tall tree.

Placing a noose over one of the branches, Saunders drove Fanning's horse from under him. For almost an hour Fanning hung there holding the rope with both hands. Finally the hands loosened and slipped from the rope.

For years afterward natives said that on moonlight nights shadowy figures could be seen hanging from the trees near the swamp. And few there were who cared to go by it after the sun had set.

Only the chimney was left standing when Sherman's bummers burned the Saunders plantation.

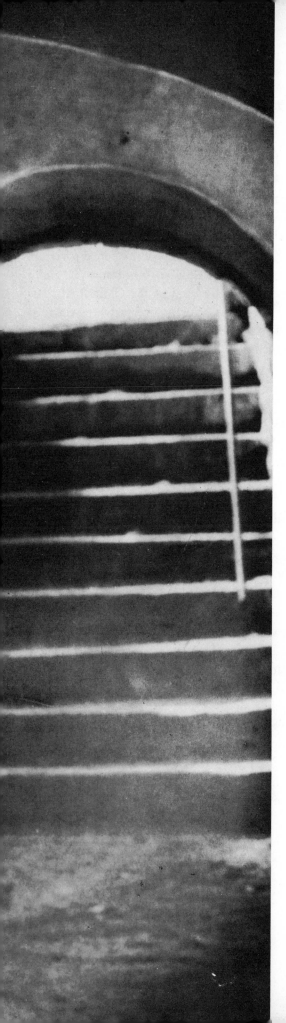

The Little Red Man

The cellar at Old Salem haunted by the playful ghost is now a tourist attraction

It was March 25th of the year 1786. Just thirteen years earlier the first Moravians had settled in Salem.

Single Brother Andreas Kremser, stood looking with quiet pleasure across the sunken garden behind the Brothers House. For some years now he had lived here with the other unmarried men of the religious community.

Like his companions, he prayed, he sang, he cooked, worked at his trade of shoemaker and occasionally gardened. Andreas looked at the

35

lovely shades of the flowers made more brilliant by the glow of twilight.

His thoughts went back to his boyhood in Pennsylvania. The long forgotten odor of spring lilacs was strong about him. He remembered his bitter longing for the parents he had never known. At the age of three he had been placed in a home and school for little boys.

Andreas was just sixteen when he had left Pennsylvania to carve out his future as a shoemaker in North Carolina. For brief intervals he had done kitchen work and even swept chimneys. But chimney sweeping was not for him and he recalled that task with irritation.

How ridiculous to criticize his chimney sweeping just because there had been an epidemic of measles. Yet that is just what had happened. But he had told them—the mayor, the civic leaders and anybody else who criticized his chimney sweeping. The chimneys were miserably constructed and there were too many for any one man to sweep.

His thoughts returned abruptly to the present and he realized it was almost dark. He must get ready to attend evening services.

That night after worship he felt wakeful and restless. There was excavating in progress in the cavernous "deep cellar" of the house where an addition was planned. Perhaps he should work for awhile before retiring. It was only about eleven.

The cellar's depths were cold and damp. There were no windows and the brothers worked by the light of the flickering candles. Taking up a shovel he joined the others. They cast long, eerie shadows as they worked to hollow out a place under the clay bank.

It was easier to work on his knees. Andreas scarcely heard the warnings of those watching that the bank was almost ready to go. Suddenly

there was a shout: "Jump back. It's breaking off!" The men threw themselves backward, but Andreas still on his knees could not rise in time.

It seemed as if tons of the damp, smothering earth descended on him. With frantic efforts his fellow workers managed to dig him out. His left leg crumpled beneath him, his whole body felt numb with pain.

Brother Lewis who was a doctor gently removed Andreas' red jacket. He opened a vein in his left arm but little blood would flow. At about two o'clock the blessing of the Church was bestowed upon him. Shortly afterward the spirit of Andreas Kremser left his body.

From that day on the brothers would oftentimes hear a sound like the tap-tap-tap of a shoemaker's hammer. Each would glance quickly over his shoulder but never saw the shoemaker at work. Occasionally as they walked through the shadowy basement passageways, the last of a red coat would flit around the curve just ahead. "There goes Kremser," one brother would whisper to another.

Finally there became less and less need for a home for unmarried brothers. The last of the brothers moved out and for awhile families made their home there.

A few years later the Church used the house for widows of the congregation. Halls which once rang with the songs of the young men now listened to the muted voices of elderly ladies reminiscing of their youth.

A child visiting her grandmother ran to tell her, "Betsy saw a little man out there and he did this." The little girl crooked her finger to show how a hand had beckoned to her.

Some of the old ladies told of glimpsing a little man with a friendly smile. But their stories were shrugged off with amusement.

Then one day a prominent man of the community was showing a friend through the old cellar. As they went he related the story of the "Little Red Man." Both were highly amused. It was not until they turned to leave that all at once—out of nowhere—there he stood.

With arms outspread the two men tried to corner him. They closed in only to grasp empty air. Eluding them, he reappeared at the end of the gloomy chamber and grinned merrily.

Several years later a visiting minister ended the career of the "Little Red Man" forever. An invocation to the Trinity and the words, "Little Red Man go to rest" exorcised the friendly chap who hasn't been seen since.

The Thing
at
The Bridge

Aaron Lee was a scholar. He couldn't explain the unearthly horror at the bridge . . . until Old Squire died

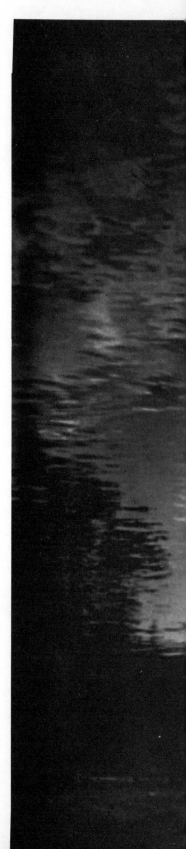

Time is such a relative thing that to an insect a few days may be a lifetime and last month eons away. To the thoughtful among us, it is but a slight strain to break the bonds of time and imagine a hot, still day in May of 1820 is our own today.

It is easy to feel the heat of that sun beating down upon our face and shoulders. And shading our eyes we see again the white man and the black man hoeing cotton together along the bank of Mill Creek in Johnson County near Smithfield.

They are master and slave. To look into the heavily lined face of Lynch is to see a face at

38

Aaron Lee felt he was not alone on the bridge.

once both ignorant and cruel. "Old Squire" has the red hair characteristic of Lynch's Negroes. The unusual hue was said to be caused by their diet. Lynch fed them on Hayman potatoes and cow tallow.

Today the black man's labors seemed only to anger his master. When he slowed for a moment's rest the lash fell across his back with a crackle. If a sprig of grass remained in the row behind his hoe, the whip curled swiftly through the air again stinging and burning like a streak of liquid fire on the sweaty, shining black flesh.

The two men continued to chop closer and closer to the bridge across Mill Creek. For a moment Squire looked up welcoming the approach of dusk. Lynch caught him at it, cursed and once again lashed out with the whip. Squire turned and the full, searing impact struck square across his face.

But this time the whip had met and ignited kindred violence. Almost of its own volition it seemed that the shining blade of the slave's hoe made a swift arc in the sunlight—an arc which ended with crushing impact on the forehead of Lynch. Without a sound he fell to the ground. For a few seconds the Negro stood over him, horrified at what he had done, still holding fast to the blood covered hoe.

Then seizing Lynch by the feet he dragged him under the bridge. He hollowed out a grave quickly in the damp earth, working with fearful urgency lest he should hear the sound of footsteps approaching the bridge. When he finished his grisly task he crawled cautiously from under the bridge and in a moment had faded into the dusk around him.

On the following day Lynch's absence was noted by his slaves, and local whites supervised a search party. The search was a fruitless one, however. And no further efforts were made as

Lynch was regarded with as little esteem by his white neighbors as by his own slaves.

Among these neighbors was a highly educated gentleman named Aaron Lee who lived on top of the hill overlooking Mill Creek. An eccentric bachelor, he devoted himself to books and breeding fine horses.

As was only natural when stories began to circulate of weird events at the bridge, the opinion of such a scholar as Aaron Lee was sought. Local folk told of the sound of trace chains rattling under the bridge at night, of torches ceasing to burn when the bearer set foot upon the bridge and mysteriously starting to blaze once more when he had crossed. On one occasion a heavy cane left a man's hand to be thrust back into it again as he reached the other side.

Finally the curiosity of the man of letters needed to be satisfied. On a late autumn afternoon he took one of his best mares and rode down the hill toward the bridge. His crossing was uneventful, and enjoying the fine weather he continued on for some distance.

It was nightfall when he reined his mount about-face and began the homeward journey. All went well until he reached the top of the long sloping hill down which flowed Mill Creek.

At that moment a cold gust of air seemed to rise from the waters of the creek and envelop both horse and rider. Simultaneously Lee felt something land on the horse behind him and cling with a heavy pressure against his back, a pressure so chilling that icy waves penetrated his very marrow.

Instantly the gait of his mare broke from a spirited canter into the slow dragging walk of a plow horse. She moved with great difficulty as if weighted down with a load almost beyond her strength. Lee's first impulse was to leap off his mount and flee from the frigid thing pressing close to his back. With a strong effort of will he held to his self-control.

At length the human rider, the horse, and its ghastly burden reached the bridge. As the mare's hoofs touched it, the terror-stricken Lee heard the most agonizing groans coming from beneath the timbers of the bridge.

It was the pain-wracked voice of a man engaged in a death struggle. And although most of the words were indistinct, one was plain. That was the word "Squire."

As the horse cleared the bridge the frightful cries stopped. But the icy rider clung close to the shrinking horseman. And the horse itself seemed near the point of exhaustion as she ascended the hill near Lee's home. As they gained its crest there was a convulsive movement from behind Aaron Lee and the thing accompanying him was gone as quickly as it had come.

Relieved of her strange burden the terrified horse leaped forward and galloped with such frantic speed that Lee had ridden two miles past his home before he was able to rein her about. When they reached home the mare was wet with foam and sweat. Her wind was broken and never again was she her former high-spirited self.

It was not long afterwards that the time drew near for Old Squire to die. In the closeness of the tiny slave cabin he fought his writhing conscience at every turn. Finally he sent a pathetic plea to the scholar on the hill, begging to see him before he died.

Aaron Lee came and he listened as the old Negro poured out his gruesome and somehow pitiable story. There was no need for Lee to question it. The meaning of the word which he had heard coming from under the bridge now fell into place.

Seeing that Old Squire had just a few hours to live he tried to reassure him as best he could. Lee left the slave's cabin shortly after nightfall, knowing the slave would never live to be brought to trial.

It was early the next morning when Lee decided to exercise one of his horses. He started down the hill toward the bridge and was but a few feet away when he saw upon it the outstretched body of a man. Riding up to it he was amazed to recognize the lifeless figure of Old Squire.

He would have sworn that the old man could not have risen from his bed, so weak was he the evening before. How had he come to arrive at this spot fully a mile from his cabin? It was a mystery Aaron Lee was never able to explain satisfactorily to himself. He became more and more withdrawn and pensive.

But he told and retold the story of his fearful ride and the end of Old Squire. During the Fifties it was a common sight at night to see a light bobbing up and down around the bridge. And those who saw it would say, "See, there is Lynch lashing Old Squire now to his heart's content."

41

Devil's Tramping Ground

No one questioned his infernal Majesty's right to this piece of ground

In this age of science there are fewer and fewer mysteries of nature that remain to challenge man. Does the Devil have favorite haunts on earth? Does he pay nocturnal visits to these spots?

Yes, say the natives who live near the "Devil's Tramping Ground" 10 miles west of Siler City.

Just off a country road near Harper Cross Roads is a perfect circle in the midst of the woods. It is 40 feet in diameter. Surrounded by pines, scrub oaks and underbrush, the circle itself is bare except for a type of wire grass.

The narrow path around the edge of the circle brooks no growth of any kind. Sticks or other obstructions put in the path are never there in the morning.

According to Chatham County natives, it is the Devil whose nightly presence discourages the growth of anything fresh and green and good. Round and round the well-worn path he paces, concocting his evil snares for mankind.

Who can tell? To the best knowledge of those living nearby, no one has yet dared to spend the night at the "Devil's Tramping Ground" and spy on his Infernal Majesty.

The Reverend Edgar Teague, a retired minister living a short distance down the road, tells of a group of young men from Bennett who dared one of their number to spend the night there. He took the dare, but Mr. Teague says that along about 11:30 as he was driving home from his brother's house, he passed a blanketed figure heading toward town as fast as his legs could carry him.

Efforts have been made to explain the circle. The most popular theory holds that it was an Indian meeting ground where roaming tribes gathered periodically for feasts and celebrations. These always included the vigorous, abandoned dancing of the braves.

The rhythmic movements of countless moccasined feet accompanied by drums throbbing through warm summer nights could well have made a bare spot. But the feet and their owners have long since been gathered to the Great Spirit while the surrounding underbrush still grows to the edge of the circle and stops.

Less glamorous is the theory that the circle was made by the hoofs of horses circling around and around to power a mill for grinding cane. This would be more feasible if there were not other similar spots now well overgrown.

Several scientifically minded investigators have noted the presence of salt nearby and concluded that the soil here had too high a sodium chloride content to encourage plant growth. This theory, however, cannot explain the perfection of the circle or the narrow path encircling its perimeter.

One of the most startling recent discoveries came when soil tests were made by the North Carolina State Department of Agriculture. Results showed the soil within the circle to be completely sterile.

This only serves to compound the mystery. Soil is known to replace itself. Why should this soil just within the bounds of the circle remain sterile from the time of the earliest settlers while just outside of it plant life abounds?

It will take further word from science to disprove Satan and among the natives it is still the gentleman with the pitchfork who casts the larger shadow at the "Devil's Tramping Ground."

44

To this day no plant or tree will grow on the spot the devil treads.

The LIGHT *at* MACO STATION

Over the years this flickering light has eluded all attempts at explanation

There was fog in the low places and out of the blackness overhead fell a fine, steady rain. It made little ponds of the ruts in the lonely country road.

Hugged by scrub pines, vines and underbrush the road straggled for perhaps a hundred yards. Then the woods stopped abruptly and there lay the wet softly gleaming rails at Maco Station.

Maco lies fourteen miles west of Wilmington on the Wilmington-Florence-Augusta line of what is now the Atlantic Coast Line Railroad. It is today much as it must have looked to Joe Baldwin a little over 90 years ago.

Joe was conductor of a train headed toward Wilmington that rainy spring night of 1867. Just fourteen miles from home his thoughts turned to his family. Would his wife be up to greet him?

Even his train sounded as if it were glad to be on the home stretch. There was something comforting about the chugging noise of its wood-burning engine. For the moment Joe forgot the shower of soot and sparks which he battled daily to keep his coaches clean.

It was time now to go through the cars ahead and call out the station. He glanced proudly at his gold railroad man's watch. The hands of the watch read three minutes 'til midnight. Just about on time.

He tugged at the door at the end of the car. The night was so dark he couldn't see the outline of the car ahead. As he managed to open the door, he swung his lantern a little ahead of his body. The foot outstretched to step forward stopped in mid-air. There was no car ahead! He was in the last coach of the train and it had come uncoupled.

47

Panic surged through him and for a moment he could hardly get his breath. His first thought was of the train which followed his own. He must signal them. They had to know there was a wild car in front of them.

He raced back through the car. With one mighty heave he wrenched open the heavy door at the rear and was out on the platform. He felt his own coach losing speed and as it did he saw the huge, fiery eye of the train which followed him.

He began to swing his lantern back and forth, back and forth more furiously as the distance between him and the advancing train grew smaller.

The pursuing train plunged on through the night, its cyclops eye burning balefully. With terrific impact it hurtled into the rear of the runaway coach completely demolishing it. In the collision Joe's head was severed from his body.

A witness said that his lantern waved desperately until the last, then rose in the air, and inscribing a wide arc, landed in a nearby swamp. It flickered there for a moment and then the flame continued burning clear and strong.

Not long afterward lovers strolling near the railroad late at night reported seeing a strange light along the tracks. It would start about a mile from Maco Station—just a flicker over the left rail. Then it would advance, growing brighter as it came up the track. Faster and faster it seemed to come swinging from side to side. There would be a pause and it would start backwards, for a moment hanging suspended where it had first appeared, and then it would be gone.

Watchers over the years have said that the light is Joe Baldwin's lantern and that Joe is hunting for his head. Once the light was gone for over a month but it always comes back. Joe seems to prefer dark, rainy nights.

After roads were built in the area, skeptics maintained that the light was merely a reflection. Several years ago all traffic in the area was blocked off while a group of observers watched for the light. Joe appeared swinging his lantern as usual.

A short time before, a company of Fort Bragg soldiers armed with rifles decided to put an end to Joe's nightly excursions. His lantern eluded both guns and soldiers.

Over the years railroad engineers have sometimes mistaken Joe's light for a "real" signal. As a result the railroad ordered its signalmen at Maco to use two lanterns, one red and one green.

And so, after 90 years, Joe Baldwin still haunts the track at Maco looking for his head.

The blood-stained rock lies in the shadow of Dromgoole Castle.

Drom-goole

At the western edge of Chapel Hill is a high wooded cliff. The view from it is beautiful, and the spot is frequented by young lovers. Why does it seem to attract tragedy?

In recent years two young men have committed suicide nearby. Not far from the cliff lies a rock with mysterious stains which resemble blood. Is this rock the only remaining clue to the untimely death of an earlier university student?

In 1833 a youth named Peter Dromgoole arrived from Virginia to study at the University. He had been there only a few months when he

49

met and fell deeply in love with a beautiful Chapel Hill girl.

There are few campuses which equal the loveliness of the University of North Carolina in the spring. It must have been particularly appreciated by young Peter Dromgoole that spring of 1833.

He and Fanny had their own secret meeting place—a huge flat rock near the cliff. Some afternoons when Fanny arrived before Peter she would sit on the rock watching the sunlight drift through the leaves above.

It was never long, however, before she would see Peter's tall figure striding toward her along the winding road which led to the rock. One balmy spring day followed another so happily that these two could hardly have sensed the approaching tragedy.

Then Peter noticed that another student — a close friend of his — was also interested in Fanny. Gradually Peter's jealousy grew until finally it became an unreasoning thing which knew no bounds.

He made every effort to avoid his former friend but the other youth seemed to delight in goading him. One afternoon the two met face to face on one of the narrow dirt walks of the campus.

His rival's shoulder hit Peter's with such force as they passed that his hat was knocked to the ground. The rage which had been smouldering within Peter rose and enveloped him. His face flushed and heated words flew between the two young men.

The other youth challenged Peter to a duel. The challenge was no sooner flung down than it was accepted.

Each chose his seconds. The spot agreed upon for the duel was to be near the cliff at the edge of the town. The hour was set for midnight and

plans were laid with the utmost secrecy.

Peter was a reasonably good shot but the night of the duel was such that marksmanship good or bad scarcely mattered.

A warm May evening, it had rained briefly and a low lying mist clung to the ground wrapping itself tenaciously around students and trees alike. The two young men and their seconds made their way carefully toward the cliff.

Before they realized it the protagonists were almost upon each other. As they backed off for the agreed upon ten paces their figures assumed an almost ghostlike quality. Two shots rang out and the seconds rushed toward the young man who lay on the ground.

Blood covered the front of the ruffled white shirt. Even as his second attempted to lift his head Peter Dromgoole gasped and breathed his last.

Terrified, his rival and the two seconds dragged the lifeless Peter away from the cliff and toward a huge rock. Digging frantically—lifting their heads at each strange sound from the woods — they finally managed to dig a grave deep enough. They lifted Peter's body from the rock, placed it in its shallow grave and replaced the earth as carefully as the darkness and their haste would allow.

Meanwhile Peter's family had received a strange letter from him. A letter which warned that he might bring sadness upon them and that they would probably never hear from him again.

This was the last they ever heard from their son. A few weeks later his uncle, at the insistence of Peter's Mother made a trip to Chapel Hill. In the room which Peter had shared with a young man named John Williams were the only signs which remained of him—his trunk and a few clothes.

Peter Dromgoole had disappeared as completely as if he had been spirited away. His fellow students were unable to give any clues as to what had happened to him. Stage coaches leaving Chapel Hill showed no record of any passenger named Peter Dromgoole.

His uncle returned to Virginia a saddened and extremely worried man. His trip had been fruitless and with not one clue to his nephew's whereabouts.

This version of Peter's death and disappearance was related by a former student as he lay on his deathbed some 60 years later. It may or may not be the true story of the strange fate of Peter Dromgoole.

But what of a Chapel Hill girl named Fanny?

For many a long summer afternoon she waited at the rock for her lover. What strange brownish stains had suddenly appeared on it! Sometimes as the shadows lengthened she would think she saw a tall figure striding toward her through the woods. Then she would put her head on her arms across the rock and sob quietly. Her agonizing questions were never to receive an answer.

According to another story young Peter ran away from school and enlisted in the army. However, the muster rolls of his supposed battalion have never been found.

Is the name of Peter Dromgoole upon them? If so, the yellowed pages lying in some forgotten cache hold fast to their secret.

*G*host of the
OLD *M*INE

A hundred years ago, Gold Hill was a boom town. And the tiny, peaceful community still remembers its violent past

Twilight is the hour to see a town if you would sense its true spirit. When evening falls in the tiny community of Gold Hill near Concord the present fades and shadows of the past begin to live again.

The superstructures of old gold mine shafts jut darkly grotesque against the sky. An immense deserted mine office building crouches brooding beside the country road.

At the village crossroads is a general store reminiscent of 50 years ago. Everything about this out-of-the-way place echoes the past. It is a shell of a once vibrant community with its heart gutted out. The stuff that once made the blood course lustily through the veins of this town was gold.

Suppose by some accident of time we should arrive in Gold Hill on a day just a little over 100 years ago. How excitingly different the town looks to our eyes. It is rowdy and bustling with the smell of smoke in the cold December air. Heavily bundled figures jostle each other along the muddy main street.

Occasional boisterous peals of laughter come from The Nugget saloon and the murmur of soft Latin voices mingles with thick Cornish brogues. Gold Hill is booming in this year of 1842. It is bursting its shoddy seams with Jew and Gentile, Latin and Nordic, Cornishmen and Negro slaves.

Rough, uneducated men are converging on it from every direction, drawn by their lust for gold. Among them Aaron Klein was a misfit. Son

53

of a Rabbi—almost too gentle for his own good—what did this young man have to do with the greed and anticipation swirling about him?

Aaron himself couldn't have explained it. His parents had died several years earlier, back in Pennsylvania. Just 20, this not quite boy, not yet man had landed in Gold Hill.

It was a week before Christmas and Aaron leaned against one of the store fronts watching a motley group stumble out of The Nugget. They might have passed him unnoticed if it had not been for the sharp eyes of "Big Stan" Cukla. His tremendous physique made the nickname well earned. And no amount of whiskey seemed able to dull his amazing bodily coordination.

For reasons of his own he had taken an intense dislike to Aaron. Some smiled slyly and said it was rivalry for the heart of a lovely, blue eyed Cornish girl named Elizabeth Moyle.

Big Stan stopped abruptly when he saw Aaron standing in the shadows.

"Have a drink little Jew boy," he called out tauntingly. Aaron made no reply. The big man's face reddened, the muscles of his short neck bulged and the ugly little eyes, too small for the coarse features, glared in hatred.

One huge arm shot out and grasped the back of Aaron's neck.

"We'll see whether you're too blasted good to drink with me," he roared. Holding a bottle in his free hand he tried to force the fiery liquid between Aaron's lips.

The youth coughed, spluttered and finally managed to free himself from the grip of his tormentor. He half stumbled, half ran toward the doorway of a store behind him.

"She doesn't want a sniveling, sick puppy. She wants a man!" were the last words Aaron heard as he reached the shop's door safely.

But Big Stan Cukla was wrong. He often bragged that he knew the shafts of the mine as well as he knew his own little shack, but he did not know women.

It could not have been more than a week later when word that Aaron and Elizabeth would marry on Christmas Eve spread among the log cabins, shacks and covered wagons of Gold Hill.

Every hour that Aaron labored in the depths of the Randolph mine he hated it more. But the odious work brought him nearer the day when he and his bride could go North and begin a new life together.

As Christmas approached, young Aaron's happiness knew no bounds. Even the days in the mine's dark tunnels seemed to fly. Before, he would think of the black nothingness of the 850 foot shaft below as the skip would lower him down to his level. Now, he hardly thought of the water and darkness in the depths beneath his feet.

The miners and their wives enjoyed joshing Aaron about his coming marriage. But there was one whom these crude but good natured jokes only made more taciturn.

Big Stan's hatred of Aaron had become a seething, burgeoning thing within him. Sometimes at the sight of Aaron it would rise in his throat as if it must find release or choke him.

A few nights before the wedding Aaron returned to his tiny shack to find that a puppy he had been caring for was gone. Calling and searching through the broomstraw back of the row of shacks he heard a whimpering sound. It came from the direction of the Randolph shaft. The whimpering ceased as he drew closer.

At the entrance to the shadowy shaft he found the still warm body of the puppy — its head crushed by a heavy blow.

And then there must have been another sound, perhaps a half-mad roar of animal-like satisfaction. On Aaron's part there could only have been a terrible surge of panic at the brute strength of his antagonist before oblivion came.

The following morning when the first of the miners arrived at the shaft they found the body of a small dog nearby. One of them dug a shallow grave for it with his pick. Accompanied by raucous laughter from his comrades he leaned on the pick handle, head bowed ostentatiously, and held a mock funeral service.

Aaron Klein did not appear for work that day and by the morrow the whole mining village knew he had disappeared as completely as if he had been translated.

Elizabeth Moyle's eyes were like dark, sad windows where someone was dying inside. Big Stan came to her father and suggested leading a search party through the countryside around Gold Hill.

"Just so youse ud be knowin' if the boy been done harm," said he.

The searchers returned cold and exhausted after walking for miles through the woods and fields and discovering not a sign of Aaron Klein.

Several months later people began seeing a ball of light near the mine shaft at night. The light would travel toward the row of shacks. Women fetching water at dusk would come in breathless saying the light had followed them. Some would say it was accompanied by a sound like a puppy whimpering.

An occasional miner returning home late at night from the Gold Nugget would swear that the light had been close on his heels every step of the way.

As the days went by money continued to be plunked with careless exuberance on the counters of the business establishments in Gold Hill. Most of these immigrants considered themselves wealthy beyond their wildest dreams.

All but Stan Cukla. When his pudgy fingers touched the gold, he touched it as if he were caressing a woman. For Big Stan had deluded himself that this yellow dust could buy him the favor of the blond Elizabeth.

Even before he had sent his rival plunging to his death in the depths of the mine shaft, the big man had worked secretly in the tunnels at night. The light from the candle on his cap would move methodically along the tunnel wall. It was a tiny flame which floated and bobbled in the sea of surrounding blackness.

Almost a year had passed since Aaron's death, when one night long after midnight, Stan Cukla was digging the precious ore. It might have been his aloneness, for sometimes the light of his own candle seemed to him to be reflected back from the darkness around him. Every so often Big Stan thought that about halfway up the tunnel he could see a light flicker. It was a light about the size of his own which moved along at the same pace he did. Only lately the light was nearer.

On this December night he was sure that he saw it again—closer still. He tried to concentrate on his work but his breath began to come faster. Soon his heart began to pound so frantically in the stillness that he could hear its beating. The light's glow appeared to travel faster along the wall.

Its tiny circle of brightness was now visible out of the corner of Big Stan's eye. Then it was at his side. He could have died rooted to the spot, but he had to turn and see it.

Before his eyes stood a dripping, faceless thing. On its cap sputtered a candle.

With a horrified cry, Cukla lunged past the figure and fled toward the skip which would lift him to safety. The light followed close behind, seeming to gain every time Cukla's heavy boots would slip on the loose shale floor of the tunnel.

Big Stan's hand finally brushed the beams which framed the mouth of the tunnel and he stepped out of it toward the skip.

But the skip was gone.

Where it should have been there was nothing but black emptiness. And the heavy, terrified body of Big Stan plummeted down – down – down.

The following morning the miners coming to work were surprised to find that the skip was not at the ground level. Pulling it up by the cables they found the body of Stan Cukla. And judging from its appearance he must have fallen many, many feet before he struck the floor of the lift.

There was much speculation as to how he had met his fate. But all any of the men actually knew was that he must have entered the mine the night before and after he had gotten off at his level the skip had somehow continued to go down until it had reached the bottom of the 850 foot shaft.

Stories about the mysterious light which seemed to come from the direction of the Randolph shaft continued to circulate for a number of years. Shortly after the Civil War it was seen no more. But the remains of the superstructure of the old Randolph mine still loom tall and sinister.

The BATTLE
of the DEAD

*In 1905 two hunters wit-
nessed a Civil War battle
fought forty years earlier*

One of the most fascinating possibilities which grips the minds of men is the re-occurrence of scenes from the past. There have been stories of midnight rides, romantic trysts and duels re-enacted. Those who claim to have seen these things can describe the appearance and action of the participants with amazing detail.

Most of the attempts to explain these strange phenomena have been based on the theory of exact duplication of atmospheric conditions. This freak of nature may occur so rarely as to be glimpsed by few mortals. But none have yet ventured to say whether these stories are in the realm of the scientific or supernatural.

Jim Weaver who lived near Smithfield in the early 1900's, never forgot the terrifying events of the night he visited the past. Weaver made no effort to explain it. He simply knew that it had happened. He was there, he saw it, and he told the story for the rest of his life.

A man of medium height and somewhat slight build, Jim Weaver was a farmer and a miller. Smithfield folk called him the "Blue Man." He was subject to a mild form of epilepsy and the nitrate of silver remedy of those days turned its users a bluish color.

The few who still remember Jim Weaver recall that he seldom cut his hair or trimmed the long black beard he wore. They remember also the sight of his bare feet, one of them missing the great and second toe. As he wielded an ax one day he had accidentally chopped the toes off and maintained ever after that the shock started his epilepsy.

Although he worked long and hard, Weaver and his family seemed always in the throes of poverty. He was a quiet, serious fellow and his only boast was that he had never told a lie.

Jim's weakness was his love for hunting. Many a night he and his dog went after the wary possum in the woods of Bentonville near his home.

Late one Saturday night in March, he and an Englishman named Joe Lewis were walking along through pine trees and thickets. When the staccato barks of Weaver's hound rent the night air, the two men knew the dog had treed a possum.

Jim Weaver had always felt a man ought not to hunt on Sunday. He glanced now at the moon sinking lower and lower in the sky. He was aware that it was probably already midnight. But there was surely a possum in that tree and he had to get it.

In order to do so he decided to chop down the small tree where the hound had stationed himself. Grasping his ax he drew back and struck a resounding blow. As he did so there came a blinding flash of light from the top of the pine. Badly startled, Jim let his ax drop from his hand and stood paralyzed with fear while one flash after another erupted in the surrounding trees.

They illuminated the woods about him. And he could see shadowy, uniformed figures running to and fro, dodging behind trees and stumps. Each carried an old fashioned rifle.

All at once from behind Weaver came the rush of horses. Gray-clad riders — a ghost cavalry — thundered past. There was the hum of bullets and the crackle of musketry. Men in blue uniforms were running, shouting, shooting from behind the trees and dying in horribly grotesque positions.

From nearby rifle pits heavy shot tore through the branches of the trees and ricocheted from their trunks with a vicious snap. Still the two men stood rooted to the spot. Their knees felt weak and their foreheads were beaded with cold perspiration. The woods all around them was full of the sound and fury of battle. Bullets hissed past them like hail and peppered trees and soldiers alike.

58

Then about ten yards away from them, Jim saw a desperate encounter take place. A Yankee soldier was attempting to wrest the flag of an advancing Confederate unit from its flag bearer. A second gray-clad figure came up to help defend the standard. The Yankee turned and with a lunge pierced him through with his bayonet.

Now the Yankee and the young Confederate soldier with the flag under his arm struggled together. Finally, hatless, his face streaked with the enemy's blood, the flag bearer suffered a knife thrust to his shoulder and fell to the ground.

Only a few minutes had probably elapsed before Jim Weaver and Joe Lewis began to run. Fear spurred them on while their hearts thudded wildly and their throats ached. They passed the old Harper House in their flight. But they did not pause to watch the balls of fire illuminating the dark sky behind it nor to marvel at the strange light streaming from the windows.

On they fled until in utter exhaustion they threw themselves flat on the ground near the kitchen house back of Weaver's log cabin.

On the night that Jim Weaver and Joe Lewis hunted among the old trenches and earthworks of Bentonville, almost forty years had passed since the Blue and Gray had fought and died there. It was on this very ground that Joe Johnston sought to prevent Sherman's 60,000 men from joining with Grant. The battle began on Sunday, March 19, 1865. It continued through Tuesday the 21st with artillery fire crackling far into the night.

The nearby Harper House was used as a hospital for the wounded and their screams had shattered and shocked and entreated for several days.

Jim Weaver has long ago joined Smithfield's Confederate veterans to whom he told his story of the night he saw the battle of Bentonville with his own eyes. Believe him or not as you will.

But there was one among these veterans who knew Jim did not lie. Only seventeen years old on that night in 1865, he had served as flag bearer for his unit. His left arm still hung useless at his side from the shoulder wound he had received while trying to retain his unit's flag. His older brother had died in an effort to help him.

The Harper house where lights were seen was used as a hospital during the war by both armies.

59

The Mysterious
Hoof-Prints at Bath

For more than 150 years the mysterious hoof-prints have been a re-minder of the harsh bargain young Jesse Elliot struck with the devil

There've been lots of tales about the hoof-prints, but it was just a simple thing. Like the marks where an automobile accident was." Old Ed Cutlar looked off his front porch toward the woods as he talked. The land he saw has been owned by the family for generations.

"Folks used to leave their horses loose down there in the woods on Goose Creek. Some fellows from Bath, 'specially one called Jesse Elliot, used to do a lot of racing on Sundays.

"This Elliot, from what I always heard, must have been a pretty high livin', reckless sort. On this particular Sunday a crowd of them was down at the creek readyin' their horses and talking about what each could do.

"Elliot jumped on his horse and started down the racing lane gallopin' like fury." Mr. Cutlar paused, and then went on: " 'Take me in a winner or take me to hell,' he shouted to his horse.

"He'd no more than said it 'til the animal leaped in the air, dug her hoofs in the dirt and threw him slam against the side of a big pine."

Jesse Elliot was killed on October 13, 1813. The story as Ed Cutlar tells it today has been handed down in his family for almost 150 years.

"When I was a child we'd pull up grass and take bark and put it in the prints on our way home from school. Next mornin' they'd be just as clean as can be.

"One time my Uncle carried corn out there. He called his hogs and threw the corn all around and in the tracks. You know they wouldn't touch the corn that fell in those hoof-marks?" Ed Cutlar stopped and pondered a moment.

"I say his death was a warnin' to people not to make such heavy impressions," was his final word on the subject.

The farmhouse of Ed Cutlar, one mile west of Bath, is 250 yards from the hoofprints. One can still see the strange looking hollow places in the ground. The holes are about the size of a saucer. And they are bare of grass or any kind of growth. A short distance from these depressions in the earth is the rotted stump of an old pine tree. It is said that hairs from young Elliot's head clung to the pine bark for months. Finally that side of the tree died leaving the other side still green and living.

Nothing covers the hoofprints for long, although many skeptics, including a newsreel cameraman named Earl Harrell, have placed debris over them. The next morning he, like countless others, returned to find the marks clean and no trace of the debris in the impressions.

A descendant of Jesse Elliot confirms the date of 1813 as that of his death. But according to the story of an old family slave it was not Sunday but Christmas Eve. In this version, an annual race was to be held January 6 and he was giving his mare a workout when he was killed.

Several years ago a man leased the area from Cutlar and set up a soft drink stand there. He roped off the place containing the hoofprints and charged admission to tourists.

Wild young Jesse Elliot may not have made a harsh bargain with the devil. Ed Cutlar and the natives of Beaufort County believe that he did. If he didn't, how else would you explain the mysterious hoofprints?

The Ghost *on the* Stairs

The beautiful old house has seen many sights since it was built in 1800...but none so strange as the lovely lady in black

It was a few years after the turn of the century. And a gay party of Fayetteville girls with their suitors surrounded the piano in the parlor of the A. S. Slocumb home.

Lovely young faces reflected the flattering light of kerosene lamps. Strains of a popular romantic ballad drifted through the halls of the ante-bellum mansion.

A young lawyer leaned against the parlor's magnificently carved marble mantel. His intellectual face was pensive. Absentmindedly his finger stroked a small nick at the mantel's corner — supposedly the result of a shot fired by General Sherman.

At the moment, however, the barrister's mind was neither on Sherman nor on pretty girls. He was absorbed by an agonizing mental struggle. Was he really happy in his chosen field? Or were his years in law school meant to be forever wasted?

Perhaps the way to resolve the warring forces within him was to be alone with his thoughts. Almost oblivious to the merrymakers, he crossed the parlor and walked toward the wide archway opening into the hall.

And then he stopped dead still — his heart caught in his throat. Something or someone was floating toward him down the stairs. It appeared to be a diaphanous feminine figure. Before reaching the foot of the stairs she hesitated a moment —then turned almost sadly and started back toward the landing.

There was the flutter of filmy black and all at once she disappeared as if rounding an invisible corner.

Overcome with amazement the young man went out into the cool spring night. In the past he had listened with amused skepticism to the strange stories told of the old house.

Built in 1800 the house was used for a short while during the 1820's as a United States bank. There were rumors during the Civil War that the old bank vault was the entrance to an underground passageway to the Cape Fear River.

A man had supposedly been murdered there before the War Between the States and his body hidden in the basement bank vault. Some said that his fiancee, dressed in mourning, went up and down the long stairway searching for her sweetheart.

Many years have passed since our friend saw the apparition on the stairs. They now resound with the happy footsteps of young career girls. Living in this beautiful old home run by the Woman's Club, they take little thought for its ghosts of yesteryear.

Occasionally they pause to admire the handsome oil painting done by the famous artist Elliot Dangerfield. His father owned the house during the 1860's. They enjoy showing visitors the impressive ballroom built by another owner John Sanford, for his wedding.

But the walls know countless secrets. They have heard many sounds.

The echo of General LaFayette's boots—the tinkle of gold coins in the bank vault—the hushed voices of Confederate soldiers — the boisterous shouts of occupying Yankee troops — the dull thud of carpet bags dropped in the hall.

The marble mantel in the parlor still has the soft sheen imparted by the hands of Italian workmen long years ago. How much have its skillfully carved figures seen?

Without a doubt they know of the lady in black and her story.

And what of the young man who saw her? He gave up his plans for a law career and entered the ministry.

Passenger
TRAIN NUMBER 9

*She was sure she had seen a horrible train wreck, but the
stationmaster said there had not been a wreck*

Do people have premonitions of fearful events which are going to happen to them in the future? How can we tell how often premonitions like this come true, especially if the people are no longer here to tell us.

The baggage master was a tall thin man with a prominent nose and fair skin so transparent the bony structure of his face could be plainly seen beneath it. His eyebrows were a sandy color tipped with gray and the blue eyes which peered out from beneath them had a surprising degree of sparkle and humor. Right now he was scrutinizing his watch observing that it was almost one o'clock in the morning and satisfied that all the baggage was loaded and the train would be leaving Salisbury for Asheville, North Carolina, in a few minutes.

The steam engine spewed forth smoke and cinders, the cry of the whistle was a thin, ear-splitting shriek in the stillness of the early morning. The baggage master's name was H. K. Linster and he was from Statesville where he usually got off for a few minutes to chat with friends. He frowned as he snapped the case of his large lavishly engraved gold watch shut and prepared to board the train. Was there a hint of reluctance in his step? Did he feel any differently tonight than on the hundreds of nights before?

But that was many years ago, early morning of August 27th, 1891 to be exact, and our story has more to do with the summer vacation trip of a family from Columbia, S. C.

There was nothing unusual about the way it all started. Pat and Larry Hayes had been planning their mountain vacation for a long time. Not that they could really afford a trip what with Larry having only been in business for himself a year, but they both knew the whole family needed it.

The borrowed camper would save money and although Pat knew little about camping, she was game to learn and the children were old enough to help. Larry was not through work until late and it was after ten when Pat put the extra bedding in the trunk and they were ready to go. Larry decided he would let Pat drive from Columbia, South Carolina, to Charlotte, North Carolina, and he would drive the next lap to Statesville which was not far from Pat's mother's home.

At the filling station where they stopped in Charlotte, the station attendant commented that one of the tires was low and Larry agreed that he should fill it with more air. By now the children were asleep and Pat laid her silver blonde head back on a pillow wedged between the seat and the door so that she could nap.

Larry drove silently, following the road almost automatically, while his thoughts were on the past year and his efforts to build up his business. Suddenly, he felt the wheel twist beneath his hand and the car begin to go toward the other side of the road. He realized the tire had blown and the weight of the trailer was making it more difficult for him to control the car. Pat was immediately awake but she did not scream or cry out. Luckily he managed to slow the car, guide it back into his own lane and off the road onto the safety of the shoulder.

Larry got out to look for the jack so that he could change the tire. He and Pat both searched the back of the car but no jack. Then Pat remembered. She had left the jack on the floor of the garage when she rearranged the camping supplies.

It was almost three o'clock in the morning, there were no cars along the road at this hour and Larry figured the best thing to do was to go for help. He remembered a country store he had noticed just before the blowout. There was a light on in the back and he suspected the store owner might live there.

The children complained drowsily, then one by one fell asleep again. Pat sat wide awake and somewhat nervous but reassured by Larry's certainty that it was only a short distance back to the store.

She heard the whistle of a train far off in the distance and as it came closer she thought of how mournful a train whistle late at night can sound. Then a light appeared, at first no bigger than a pinpoint, and she watched it advance closer and closer until it was just a few hundred yards from the car.

It was the headlight on the engine and she could now see the engine and the coaches quite clearly. The train had begun to cross the bridge and had just reached the center when she was aghast to see the engine, cab and coaches give a convulsive lurch, leave the track and hurtle through the air, plunging off the bridge down into the darkness and out of sight. There were crashing, wrenching sounds as metal and wood tore asunder and cars smashed against each other.

This was followed by the most frightful screams, men's and women's voices intermingled, pleading for help. Horror-stricken, Pat jumped out of the car and began running in the direction from which the screams came. When she reached the bank of the stream and looked down below her, it was a sickening sight. The engine, tender, coaches and pullman cars were a huge pile of debris jutting out in every direction and completely damming up the creek.

People were climbing through broken windows, some being pulled through by those who had crawled out first and there were yet others who had fallen into the stream and were trying to swim to the bank. Adding to the danger and perilous situation of survivors was the fact that,

dammed up by the wreckage, the water in the stream was rising and entering the railroad cars.

In the midst of all the cries and groans Pat became aware that there was a man standing next to her. He was dressed in what must have been a railroad uniform and beneath the visor of his hat she could see that his face looked extremely white. No wonder, after what this poor man had just gone through.

"Can you give me the time, Ma'am? I would like to check my watch and see if it is running properly," said the trainman. He was gazing down at a large gold watch which she noticed with surprise looked just like the old-fashioned watch her grandfather used to show her when she was a child. But, no doubt, railroad men still carried watches like this.

"It is five minutes past three," she replied. "I wish I could go for help, but we just had a blowout and I will have to wait until my husband comes back." The man looked at her strangely and did not answer. She began to feel very much afraid. Then his face started to blur and she thought, I must be going to faint, that is why his face seems to be fading away like this.

At that moment she heard the slam of a car door and voices behind her. There was Larry and someone was with him. She ran toward them.

"Larry, there's been a terrible train wreck!"

she cried out. Larry and the stranger held a flashlight before them and the three made their way as quickly as possible in the direction she led them over at the side of the bridge. They looked down.

"Where? What in the world are you talking about? There's no train wreck down there," said Larry, the beam of his flashlight probing the stream and the banks.

"For heaven's sake, honey, you've just had some kind of nightmare. This is Mr. Bradley. He's come to help me fix the tire. Come on now, let's go back to the car. You probably fell asleep and when you woke up your dream was real to you."

Dazed, Pat got into the car, and checked the children. They were still asleep, completely unaware that anything unusual had happened.

On the way to her mother's home, Pat told Larry about seeing the train approach, the horrifying wreck and the trainman who had come up to the car. He promised to go by the railroad station the next morning and, if she wished, even back to where she was so certain she had seen the wreck. Larry was still convinced, however, that she had fallen asleep and dreamed about the wreck and the trainman who had asked her what time it was.

The next day they went by the railroad station. The old man at the counter listened while Pat told him about the train going off the track.

"No, there was no wreck last night. There hasn't been a wreck in years on that stretch of track."

"At least not since the wreck of 1891," he said. "My father used to talk about that wreck. It was the most terrible train wreck that ever happened in this state. The train had left Salisbury for Asheville and it got to Bostian's Bridge about three o'clock in the morning. It must have been a dreadful sight to see. They say the train engine and coaches just plunged right off the track and down ninety feet into the stream below the trestle. My father got out there pretty soon and he saw people climbing out the windows and calling for help. But what made it even worse was the coaches dammed up the stream and lots of those people drowned."

"It happened . . . let's see. That's odd. Looks like it was about fifty years ago. I think there's a clipping from an old paper called The Charlotte Chronicle in a scrapbook in my drawer."

He rummaged in the drawer, producing a scrapbook full of clippings about promotions, retirement pictures, building renovations and other miscellaneous news affecting the railroad over a period of many years. Finally, he came to a yellowed clipping from The Charlotte Chronicle of August 28, 1891. It was headlined, "Hurled to Death, Thirty Killed, Many Injured. At Three O'clock in the Morning, Bridge Near Statesville The Scene of the Wreck."

"You know the baggage master, a man named H. K. Linster from right here in Statesville, was killed in the wreck. He usually got off and chatted with my dad for a few minutes. What a terrible thing that must have been. I sure would hate to have seen it."

Pat Hayes' face turned white and her head began to swim. It seemed that the inside of the railroad station was beginning to go around and around. She held on to the edge of the counter and closed her eyes for a minute. But that was worse! For then she could see the light of a train followed by the engine and the coaches as they twisted and lurched before they hurtled off the track and down into the darkness. The lights in the coaches streaked through her mind like fireworks going off and again and again she could hear the screams.

"Lady, lady, are you all right?" The station master was holding her elbow.

"I didn't mean to upset you none. After all, that wreck happened fifty years ago. In fact, it was exactly fifty years ago last night."

The LITTLE People

"I saw them with my own eyes. They were on the mountain, they were near the rock . . . they were everywhere!"

There are still some wild and unexplored places left in the mountains of Western North Carolina and one about which many weird tales continue to be told is Hickory Nut Gorge near Chimney Rock.

The gorge is a challenge to even the most bold and experienced. There are precipitate cliffs, narrow ledges to scale and dizzying heights, and the reward may be bottomless pools, spectacular waterfalls seen by few and grotesque rock formations.

Not far from this gorge on the thirty-first of July 1806, a Presbyterian minister and teacher at Newton Academy sat at his desk preparing his lesson for the following day's classes. He was so absorbed in his work that it was almost eight o'clock when he realized the light had gone and the pleasant breeze which had stirred the curtains at the window next to his desk now had an icy bite.

He closed the window, found the white china matchbox, lit the kerosene lamps and touched a match to the fire. As the flames blazed up he heard footsteps on the porch and an agitated pounding at his door.

Hurrying through the dark hall he bumped into the sharp, curving arms of the coat rack on his way to the front door. When he opened it there stood his friend, Robert Searcy.

"I don't know how to tell you what I have just seen," said Searcy. "You may not even believe me, but I saw them with my own eyes. They were on the mountain, they were near the rock, they were everywhere! May I come in and sit down?" His face was white and he appeared genuinely shaken.

"Of course, you may. But who in the world are you talking about and what have you seen?"

"Well, no matter how I tell you about this it is going to sound like I have lost my mind, but probably the best thing for me to do is start at the beginning. As I sat on my porch reading after an early supper, Mrs. Reaves' girl came running up to tell me there was a crowd of people flying around on the side of the mountain near the Rock and to come right away. I simply dismissed what she said as probably some children playing a prank.

"But a few minutes later Mrs. Reaves herself came and begged me to go with her to see the 'ghosties' as she called them. This poor superstitious woman is really upset, I told myself, and deciding that the kindest thing I could do was to go with her to calm her, we started toward the mountain. After a few minutes she said, 'Do you see them?'

"I saw nothing at all and told her so. We walked a little further and she grasped my arm saying, 'There they are. Look! Over there.' This time as I looked toward the Chimney, I was absolutely amazed for south of Chimney Rock and floating along the side of the mountain was a huge crowd of white, phantom-like beings. Their clothing, and filmy as it looked, I can only call it 'clothing,' was so brilliant a white it almost hurt my eyes to

look at them. But they appeared to be human, for I could see that there were men and women and children, all sizes of beings, even infants.

"As I watched, two of them who appeared to be men went on ahead of the crowd, coming quite close to the Rock, and then vanished."

"What a frightening experience," said Newton.

"No, that is the oddest part of it," replied Searcy. "Although I felt weak, somehow, it left a solemn and pleasing impression on my mind. But you must think I have surely gone crazy. Tell me, is that what has happened? Is this the beginning of some strange insanity?"

Robert Searcy searched his friend's face anxiously for an answer. Smoke curled upward from Newton's pipe. He frowned thoughtfully and looked toward the window with its drawn curtains as if he were trying to see through them and out to the gorge for a glimpse of the mysterious beings Searcy had described.

"Don't just sit there! Tell me, friend. Am I going insane?" shouted Searcy.

"No, no. Now calm down," Newton raised one hand palm outward toward his friend. "You are not going crazy at all. You have simply seen a sight that only a few people have ever been privileged to witness. A sight so spectacular that stories about it have been told for generations among the Cherokee Indians. You recall that this whole area was once the country of the Cherokee Nation."

"For heavens sake, George, do I need a history lesson at a time like this? What does that have to do with the white figures I saw floating along the mountainside?"

"I am telling you this because the Cherokees knew about them."

"Knew about who?"

71

Chimney Rock where the Little People were seen on several occasions.

"The Little People. Do you think that something like you saw this afternoon has never happened before? Of course it has. Rare, yes, and it may have been years ago and it may not happen for many years hence."

"The gorge was the gateway to the country where the tobacco the Indians wanted for their pipes grew. It was always a frightening place to the Indians, but it was not so much the difficulties of travelling through it, the bottomless pools, the eerie rock formations which appear to us like frightful giants of another age. Nor was it the savage force with which the wind sweeps through that gorge, tearing away plants and leaving the rock bare. Oh, no. It was not these things that kept them from travelling through the gorge to reach the land where the tobacco grew. It was the spirits, the little people themselves or whatever you wish to call them, that guarded the gateway through the mountains."

"Tonight you have seen what no man may see again for years. I don't know how to explain them. You say that you saw men, women and children. If they were a mirage it is strange that a mirage would have stayed in the area long enough for Mrs. Reaves to have sent her daughter, then come after you herself. Also, a mirage is more often seen by one person, perhaps due to their physical or mental state at the moment, rather than by several."

"Could these 'beings' be angels?" asked Searcy.

"Angels? I really don't know. I have never been a great believer in spirits from another world making themselves visible in our own, but if I had been fortunate enough to see that fantastic crowd of white robed figures floating across the mountainside as you did this afternoon, I might change my mind!"

"You must see it, too. It was tremendous! When do you think it might happen again?"

"My dear Robert, how am I possibly to guess when it will happen again. We have no idea what causes them to appear. But, I would say that it is possible for the same conditions present this evening to occur at another time and when they do, whoever is near the Rock will see the figures just as you did."

Mr. Newton's prediction has come true on more than one occasion since.

In 1811 a similar phenomenon was seen. So large was the crowd that some compared it to a battle with "swords flashing" but this was probably inaccurately described. Again, shortly after the Civil War the entire countryside talked of seeing The Little People.

But the phenomenon is reported only rarely and probably when someone does see it, they are reluctant to talk of the experience, especially in these days of technology and the computer.

Some scoffers have suggested that all that was ever seen in the gorge were cloud formations, although we wonder whether intelligent observers can mistake clouds for "men, women and children."

The Phantom RIDER of the CONFEDERACY

The General reached for his pistol and aimed it at the oncoming rider when to his astonishment he saw the scores of bullet holes in the cape which floated in the wind

It is really a shame that Ichabod Crane and the Headless Horseman on the Tarrytown Road in New York ever managed to get so much publicity for the headless horseman. For the horseman there was a trickster who carried a pumpkin under his arm and not a head.

For years while people have been reading about this nonsense up at Tarrytown, they have ignored the real Phantom Rider of the Confederacy who rides a palomino stallion. She wears gossamer garments which float behind her and her blond hair streams in the wind. Both hands grasp the reins as she comes out of the past, is visible only briefly, and vanishes into the darkness as if all the legions of another world were in pursuit.

The main highway South through Arden and Fletcher past the old Calvary Episcopal Church has long since been paved. But this has not stopped the pounding of the palomino's hoofbeat which can be heard on the shoulder of the road.

Reverend Charles Stewart McClellan, Jr., writing in the Southern Tourist Magazine in December 1926, was the first writer to compare the Phantom Rider of the South with the Legend of Sleepy Hollow.

"There is a horseman who often rides through the night around old Calvary Church at Fletcher."

He tells the story of a very beautiful girl who lived near the church and was in love with a Confederate soldier whom her family refused to let her marry. Eventually, her suitor was ordered away to join Braxton Bragg's army at Chattanooga and her parents still held steadfast to their decision that she would never marry a Confederate.

During the days of the war the well at Calvary Church where she met her suitor was called "the wishing well" and local legends said that if you wished hard enough before you drank from the well your wish would come true. Even after he had gone she often went to their meeting place. But the day came when she received word that her beloved had been killed.

So, the story goes that our maiden did not wish to live but only to join the one she loved. Her father paid little heed when she told him her wish

73

would come true and so it did, just as if she had willed her own death.

The evening after the funeral service the Jenkinses sat in silence on the porch of their farm home near Fletcher Road. It was early autumn and the leaves of the dogwood trees, already turned a brilliant red, fluttered in the wind. It appeared as if the air, which was especially cold, came from among the pine trees in the church yard and the graveyard with its freshly covered grave.

The wind blew in such gusts that a faint chiming sound seemed to come from the church bells. And then in the distance came the pound of hoofbeats. On and on they came. Past the church, past the graveyard, riding with a strange, inexorable quality straight toward the Jenkins home.

Jenkins had never seen such an awesome sight. The hoofs scarcely seemed to touch the ground. But what terrified him was the palomino horse. For it was the horse of Lieutenant C. A. Walpole and on the horse was a young woman wearing a Confederate cavalry cape to protect her against the cold. He recognized now both the horse and rider. The girl was his daughter buried only the day before and the horse had been sent by the spirit of the young lieutenant to bring her.

Her last wish by the old well had come true.

Directly in front of Jenkins, the horse and its rider stopped. But while the horse stood motionless the wind and dust swirled up in a cloud and from it a voice spoke.

"Father, you have doomed me to ride forever. Do you know how bitter cold the wind is?" and leaves swept fiercely about the horse's hooves.

"Next spring General Stoneman and his troops will be here. They will burn your farm thinking you are a Confederate sympathizer because I will lead them here and they will chase this horse to your barn."

74

And it came about just as the girl had said. For in the spring of 1865 General Stoneman and his men rode into Fletcher just as dusk was falling across the graveyard and the shadows of the tall pines lay upon the tombstones.

The General was in an angry mood. His advance scouting party had been ambushed on the outskirts of Asheville and the major, who had barely escaped with his life, was describing how he and his men had been lured into the trap chasing a Confederate courier on a palomino horse.

"And the strangest thing happened. Just as the horse was about to pull away from us it turned and started to charge back. I ordered my men to stop and every trooper fired at the rider. The horse reared up as if to laugh at us and then from both sides of the road we were ambushed. Twenty-three of my men were killed. I chased after the rider and I fired my pistol six times. I have never missed my mark before and those bullets went right through him."

General Stoneman was obviously upset and irritated.

"Major, you must be extremely overtired and overwrought. I will dispatch Captain Butler to track down the rider."

A short time later the Captain picked up the trail of a single horse and followed it to a farm not far from Calvary Church. The farm belonged to a man named Jenkins who had died that winter. Butler searched the area but could not find the lone rider. However, he believed that the farm was being used as a refuge by the Confederates so he set fire to not only the house but the buildings around it.

From his headquarters camped at Calvary Church, General Stoneman wandered over to the well. It was past midnight, but the general still could not sleep. It was very seldom any of his men were ambushed and he was puzzled by the conduct of his commanding officer who was noted for his excellent marksmanship.

"I wish I could see that rider myself," he mused as he reached down and picked up the dipper at the well. The instant the water touched his lips he saw the flames rising from the Jenkins farmhouse and congratulated himself on a problem solved.

As he turned to walk back across the church yard to his headquarters tent, a dark rider galloped across the field. For a moment he thought it was Butler so he did not call out to the sentries. But the rider did not slow, and then, in a split second, he realized the figure mounted upon the horse was not a Union soldier.

He reached for his pistol and aimed it at the horseman's head when to his astonishment he saw that the rider was a woman and there were scores of bullet holes in the cape which floated in the wind behind her. He lowered his gun and watched as horse and rider rushed past him and disappeared down the road. So quickly had the horse come and gone that even the startled sentries had not been able to fire.

There were many things the general knew about war and he was not about to lose another man chasing a ghost. Not a single rider did General Stoneman dispatch to give chase. He looked at the red glow of the flames in the sky and as the road turned and rose at the crest of the hill for a brief second the ghostly rider was silhouetted in the crimson of the horizon. Strangely enough this was the only building ever burned in the Fletcher area.

A few weeks later the war came to a close and the stories of the phantom rider were classified with this period when emotions ran high and violence filled the air.

But, according to Reverend McClellan some years later, two young men of Fletcher were riding along the ridge road one night and one, as he was adjusting his stirrup strap, heard the approach of another horse. As he stood next to his own mount he could clearly see the phantom rider who dashed up to him, gazed curiously at him for a moment, and then galloped away into the night. He also tells of a farmer returning to the Fletcher settlement very late one night who was drowsy and fell asleep on his horse. The horse knew the road and kept on but suddenly the farmer was awakened by the clatter of a horse's hooves.

When he awoke and saw the Rider he sank into unconsciousness and the next day when he came to in his barn, he told his friends the story of his midnight encounter with the Phantom Rider.

And so, there will probably always be accounts of hoofbeats in the night and a mysterious figure on horseback amidst the wooded quiet of Calvary Church, and the old graveyard will continue to provide a refuge for the ghosts of those who frequented this area during its violent and colorful past. A past when the Phantom Rider of the Confederacy, with her cape blown by the wind, sped through the night down the old Fletcher Road, her steed's hoofbeats in the distance coming closer and closer, past the church, past the graveyard, riding on and on and on.

The old Church is still there, the graveyard, the road—and when the night is dark and windy, who knows who else?

The iron gates at the end of the church drive never barred the Phantom Rider.

THE DEMON *of* WIZARD CLIP

The devil ensnares the sons of men in strange and devious ways. And down to this very day the memory of the evil wrought by one of his minions still hangs like a dank fog over an ancient village in West Virginia.

The village bears three names, Smithfield, Middleway and oddest of all—Wizard Clip.

Through it ran the principal wagon route from Baltimore to Southwest Virginia, Kentucky and Tennessee. But the wagoneers have long been dead. With them died the fortunes of Wizard Clip and the man who helped it get its name.

Our story starts near the beginning of the nineteenth century with a Pennsylvanian named Livingstone. Leaving his native state he and his family purchased a lakeside farm on the outskirts of the town we have mentioned. In front of his farm and beside the Opequon River ran the wagon road.

A man of mild temperament, the Pennsylvanian was fond of contrasting with a certain modest air his former failures and the success he was enjoying in his new home.

Although Livingstone himself was liked well enough by his neighbors, the same could not be said of his wife. She was a woman of mean and dominating disposition who kept much to herself.

The Livingstones had lived only a few years in their new home when the event which was to cause their undoing befell them. Appropriately enough it happened on a most miserably cold and rainy night. Gusts of wind screeched plaintively outside the Livingstone's windows and tore with icy fingers at the shutters.

They had readied themselves for bed and were about to ensconce themselves under their feather comforters when Mrs. Livingstone heard a faint sound on the porch, quickly followed by a loud knock.

Her husband went to the door, cautiously cracking it open a few inches, only to have the force of the wind wrest it from his hand. In front of him stood the tall figure of a man, cloak swirling madly about him in the gale.

"I pray you will give me a night's lodging, sir," begged Livingstone's visitor. "My wagon has suffered an accident to a wheel and cannot be repaired before morning."

"We are about to retire but will be glad to have you pass the night with us," replied Livingstone although he could see the dour look on the face of his wife.

The stranger came in and without much grace Mrs. Livingstone showed him to his room.

The house had not been settled and quiet for long when in addition to the eerie wail of the wind another sound could be heard. It was a succession of fearsome groans interspersed with the sharp outcries of a man in pain. Stopping only to jerk on his slippers, Livingstone hurried to the door of the stranger's room and asked him if all was well with him.

In a tortured voice his guest replied that he

All around them people could hear the clip-clip of the demoniacal shears

was deathly ill and did not expect to live to see daylight. He begged his host to summon a Catholic priest that he might be given the last rites, admitting that he had neglected his religion in health, but now, in extremis, felt in dire need of its consolation.

Livingstone replied that he knew of no priest nearby and couldn't hope to find one closer than Maryland. He remarked, however, that his neighbors—the McSherrys and the Minghinis—were Catholic and perhaps could tell him of one.

His wife was by now listening to the conversation and at this she became extremely angry.

"If you think you are going to start out on any such wild goose chase in the middle of the night, I shall take good care to thwart you," said she. "And even if you should succeed in finding one, I warn you, no Romish priest shall ever set foot in my house!

"The best thing you can do is return to your bed. I'll wager this guest of ours will be as well as you or I by morning. And if I have my way he shall be on his way with the sun's first rays."

Livingstone reluctantly gave in to his wife and went back to bed.

All night the pitiful pleas and outcries continued. Next morning their guest did not appear and, much alarmed, Livingstone entered his room.

The stranger was dead.

Of course, a story had to be decided upon to tell the neighbors. The Livingstones simply said that a wayfarer had asked lodging with them the night before and died in his sleep. They made no mention of his dying wish. They recalled with surprise that he had not told them his name and, search his belongings as they would, no clue could be found to his identity.

A simple funeral was held late the following evening and the unknown traveler laid to rest. The family had no sooner returned home and

were gathered around the fire discussing the day's events when the logs in the fireplace began to writhe and jump as if in agony.

Soon they were whirling all about the room in a horrible sort of dance. After them danced Livingstone trying to catch them and heave them back into the fireplace. But no sooner would he return them than what seemed to be an almost demoniacal power would toss them out again.

This went on all night long and the terrified family did not get a moment's rest.

The following morning the worn out Livingstone went down to the highway in front of his house. He had just reached the road when he was accosted by an irate wagoneer who had stopped his team there.

"What the devil do you mean barring a public road with a rope?" cried the fellow. "Untie it from those trees, you rascal."

Livingstone rubbed his tired eyes in bewilderment. He was sure the man was drunk for he could see no rope at all. Becoming more furious by the minute the driver drew a knife and made as if to approach Livingstone. But instead he slashed at the air before him.

Now it was the wagoneer's turn to be amazed. For his knife met no resistance at all. Only airy nothingness. While he stood there in bewilderment debating what to do next another team arrived and its driver went through the same performance with the same outcome.

At length Livingstone mildly suggested that they drive on regardless of the spectre rope, and this they did. But all that day each new arrival brought Livingstone a fresh cursing. And so it kept up for several weeks.

By now it was obvious to the Livingstones and their neighbors that the strange events taking place could only be the work of a demon. And soon the Livingstones began to be harassed in yet another way. A sharp clipping noise as from a pair of invisible shears could be heard throughout

The turnpike in front of the Livingstone house looked much like this road near Wizard Clip.

and around the house. Worse yet all the family clothes and table linens were cut with crescent-shaped slits.

When visitors arrived to condole with the Livingstones they would find even the handkerchiefs folded in their pockets covered with the crescent shaped tears. And all around them they could hear the incessant clip-clip of the demoniacal shears.

On one occasion a lady visitor was complimenting Mrs. Livingstone on the fine flock of ducks waddling through the yard on their way to the Opequon River. "Clip-Clip" went the uncanny, invisible shears and, one after another, each duck's head fell to the ground, cleanly decapitated before the ladies' very eyes.

Stories of the "Wizard Clip" were spreading far and wide. And the young men of the neighborhood, eager to show how fearless they were, talked Livingstone into letting them hold a dance there. Despite the terrors of the place curiosity led many young ladies to attend.

One blustering fellow came all the way from Winchester carrying his rifle. He was determined to show off his bravery to his girl and bragged of what he would do to anything trying to clip him. All went smoothly for awhile when suddenly "clip-clip" went the devilish shears and the Winchester hero felt something flap against the back of his legs.

Much to his humiliation he was forced to retreat backwards through the nearest door while the girls looked coyly in another direction.

By this time poor Livingstone was rapidly losing heart and even his wife's masculine courage was dwindling. One night he had a dream.

He thought he was standing at the foot of a hill on top of which stood a man dressed in flowing black robes. The man appeared to be engaged in some sort of religious ceremony. As he looked at him he became aware of the presence

81

of a disembodied voice near him. The voice whispered that the man on the hill could relieve him of the torture he and his family were undergoing.

Believing the garb to be that of a priest, Livingstone immediately sought aid from the Minghinis and the McSherrys. He found that a certain Father Cahill would shortly be at Shepherdstown, about ten miles away, to hold Catholic services.

His neighbors promised Livingstone an introduction to the priest and on the day specified they accompanied their unhappy neighbor to the church meeting.

Livingstone recognized the priest immediately as the figure in his dream and falling down on his knees begged him for help. As tears streamed down his face he poured out the story of his heartlessness toward the stranger and all that had happened thereafter.

Cahill was a big-fisted Irishman not averse to an encounter even with the devil himself. So he consented to accompany Livingstone and do all he could to relieve him.

When he arrived at the Livingstones' home Father Cahill got down on his knees and, holding a small cross in his hands, prayed fervently. Then he sprinkled holy water on the threshold of the house.

"Now you must take me to the place the stranger is buried," said the priest. Together they went to what is now the old burying ground of Wizard Clip.

As the priest consecrated the grave there was the sound of a great rushing wind through the trees overhead. His robes billowed out from his body, lending an eerie, winged look to the black-garbed figure.

And the bottomless waters of the nearby lake seethed turbulently as if embracing its own. Close to the village of Wizard Clip the dark waters still hold their secret. The wizard is gone but somehow one has the feeling he may not be far off. And if walking through the village on a rainy

afternoon about dusk doesn't convince you the story is true then go to the county clerk's office in Charles Town, West Virginia.

There in the yellowing deed book is the very paper whereby in gratitude to Father Cahill and his successors Livingstone deeded thirty-four acres of land for the exorcising of the fiend. To this day the land is known as "Priest's Field."

ROOM FOR ONE

...ORE

The coachman called "room for one more," and this time the invitation seemed to be meant for her!

It seemed impossible to the girl getting off the plane from New York which had just taxied into the Atlanta airport that such a thing as New York and a real southern plantation could actually co-exist in the 1950's.

In the late summer she had met Ruthanne Reeves on a vacation trip to Greece and the two girls had returned to New York on the same plane. Ruthanne went back to her plantation home in Georgia and Elise Barnhardt to her work with a New York publishing firm.

Ruthanne and "brother John" as she called him, greeted Elise gaily and as they walked toward John's tiny sports car brother and sister kept interrupting each other with talk of parties and plans for the weekend. The car sped along one country road after another, seldom going through anything but villages with a few houses and a country store or two at the crossroads.

It was dusk and for a few minutes there was that intense light in which everything takes on a glow all its own. The fragile, spider-like cleome flowers in front of the dark gray unpainted little shacks were a vibrant pink. The cotton fields could not have looked more green.

There was a dreamlike quality about the drive as they passed one shack after another with their rusty tin roofs, sitting lonely, back from the road in the midst of a few pine trees. Then they turned down a dirt road and drove through swamps which hummed and chirped with dusk's surge of life, past gates protecting private roads, and on and on. Finally, they turned down one of these, passing through an open iron gate. Sweet gum and pine branches flicked the side of the car until the woods abruptly ceased.

Ahead lay a long avenue of moss-draped live oaks and beneath these huge old trees it was always twilight. Under this leafy, moss-draped ceiling a shadowy stillness had settled in broken only by the occasional, mournful sound of a dove.

The last rays of the sun disappeared as the car pulled up in front of an immense, sprawling southern mansion. Tall columns at the front and wings at each side made it look like some grand and dignified creature crouched nobly on its haunches. Lights were flickering on now in the rooms of the house and as the three young people entered the large center hall Ruthanne's mother, a short, cheerful little woman, plump as a marsh hen, greeted them warmly.

That evening friends arrived from nearby towns and plantations for an extremely gay dinner party and dance on the rear piazza which overlooked the river. Elise was entranced. She watched the shimmering trail of the full moon on the black waters of the river with a delightful young man who managed to make her feel completely feminine and devastatingly attractive.

The party was over shortly after twelve and the girls were tired, so by one-thirty all was quiet. Elise should have fallen asleep quickly but she did not. Her trip, the events of the evening, and even the quiet, so different from all the noises of a city at night, were enough to make her more wakeful. She tossed restlessly on the high four-poster mahogany bed, heard the grandfather clock in the hall strike two and swung her feet over the side of the bed, deciding to get up and draw back the drapes slightly, hoping for a cool breeze.

At that moment she heard a clatter outside which to her startled ears sounded like the clatter of horses' hooves. Reaching the window she drew the drapes and looked out. She could hardly believe her eyes. Directly beneath her window in the circular drive stood an impressive gold and black stagecoach drawn by four gleaming black stallions. Beside it stood a coachman dressed in black coat and britches. The entire scene was illuminated by the light of the full moon. Holding the door of the coach open with one hand, the coachman gestured toward the house with the other and called out—"Room for one more!"

Amazed, she stared down at his face. The skin was swarthy and the lips full above the jutting chin. A long scar staggered irregularly across the man's left cheek, running from the corner of his eye to his mouth.

Before she could recover from her surprise both coach and coachman seemed to literally dissolve into the darkness and disappear. She did not fall asleep until the day broke, she was so frightened, and the next morning she was quite late in awakening. Ruthanne teased her about the young man she had danced with so frequently the night before and whether she had not tired herself out. Elise smiled somewhat wanly. She was embarrassed yet she felt that she would be more so, if she tried to tell her friend she had seen an old-fashioned carriage and coachman in front of the house in the middle of the night.

That evening everyone gathered again to swim in the river and cook supper along the shore. They were all warm and friendly but as it grew dark, Elise found herself growing somewhat depressed and uneasy; however, she forced herself to talk and joke and somehow the evening passed. At eleven everyone left and the two girls sat down over a glass of iced tea and cookies to talk. But soon Elise felt so irresistibly sleepy that she

could not stay up any longer so she told her friend good night.

She fell asleep almost immediately and when she awoke, although it was only about an hour later, she did not know where she was or why she had waked up. In a moment or two she recognized the tall bedposts in the light from the moon streaming in the window and realized she was not in her New York apartment but in the bedroom of the plantation house. From without there came the rhythmic clatter of horses' hooves. She got up quickly and went over to look out. There below the window was the same scene of the night before, the striking black and gold coach and the figure of the coachman standing beside it, holding the door open with a flourish.

"Room for one more!" she heard him call out and tonight as he did so he looked up toward her window and smiled. But the smile was horrifying and made the scar on his cheek stand out with an almost purplish hue in the moonlight. "Room for one more," came the call again and this time the invitation seemed to be meant for her!

Then the coach vanished as mysteriously as it had the night before. Elise was so terrified she literally began to tremble as she sat on the edge of her bed. She did not know whether to leave her room and awaken Ruthanne or whether she would be able to conquer her fear and wait until morning. She went back to the window and looked out but where the coach had stood there was now nothing at all except a pattern of shadows cast by the moonlight upon the white gravel of the drive. A breeze rustled softly through the magnolia leaves and other than that, most of the small night sounds seemed to have fallen asleep. All was quiet and finally Elise, too, slept.

The following morning Elise was so exhausted that it was not hard for her to convince Ruthanne she was not feeling well and would like to return to New York. Ruthanne and John were disappointed but considerate enough to help her in every way. Elise had not been able to get a reservation from New York on the flight she wanted. Now she insisted she would go on stand-by.

When they arrived at the airport she bought her ticket and was told that even though the plane was full, there was always the chance a passenger might not arrive. No one else had gotten there before her to stand by and she would have the first available seat. They watched the big silver plane taxi up. Passengers got off and other passengers with their reservations got on.

As she walked toward the gate she saw the retreating back of the attendant going to the plane to check with the stewardess on whether it was full. She chatted with John and Ruthanne more cheerfully now that she knew she was away from the plantation and would be back in her own apartment that night. This busy airport seemed far away from the world of the Old South as she waited to see whether she would get a seat. Now the gate attendant was returning from checking to see whether there were any empty seats. She heard him call out.

"There is room for one more."

Elise felt a sense of shock go through her entire being. She moved forward so that she could get a better look at the man's face and as she did so he looked directly at her and repeated, "Room for one more!" His eyes met hers and there was a strange half-smile in them. His skin was swarthy, the lips full and red above a jutting chin. A scar ran across his left cheek. It was the face of the driver of the coach! The coachman who had come for her two nights in succession.

Almost hysterical, she asked her friends to take her back to the waiting room. She knew that she was not going to take that plane no matter how eager she was to get home. There was nothing she could do now but tell Ruthanne and John about her experience of the past two nights and they were astounded for neither of them had ever seen the coach or the mysterious coachman, and the plantation had been their home since childhood. However, they were quite sympathetic and it was decided that Elise should wait for a later plane and meanwhile the three would have dinner.

When it was time for her plane to depart they went back to the same gate. All three were curious to see whether the same attendant would be there. Instead they saw a thin, blonde young man with a lightly tanned complexion and a pleasant smile looking over the group of people huddled near the gate waiting for the plane to fill and hoping for a seat.

"Where is the other fellow who has the scar across his face?" Elise asked the gate attendant.

"What fellow with a scar on his face?"

"He was here for a flight to New York which left from this gate at twelve-thirty," Elise replied.

"That's impossible, I remember being on this gate myself because when I went to the plane to check on the number of passengers, I was delayed getting back. I stopped to help the stewardess with a door which was sticking. When I did return and called out that there was room for one more, a man with a briefcase under his arm got on the plane. We don't even have anyone like you describe working for us, miss."

Elise told her baffled friends good-by and got on her plane. The take-off was a beautiful one and the trip back to New York uneventful. That night she was too exhausted even to wonder about the strange events of the weekend. She decided she would think about them later and went on to sleep. The next morning she opened the door of her apartment to bring in her milk and morning newspaper. Glancing at the paper she saw the headline "Plane Crashes on Way to New York."

She read the story. The plane had left the same airport she had early yesterday afternoon. It was the flight which had "Room for one more!"

TAVERN of TERROR

It was a stop on the drover's trail along the winding French Broad River . . . but for some it was the last

There is a stretch of river on the French Broad from Painted Rock near Hot Springs to a place near Marshall, North Carolina that is one of the most beautiful, scenic and wild valleys of eastern America.

It is also a haunted land, eerie even while the sun casts shadows upon the high cliffs and reflects dancing lights upon the river's waters. Standing down by the river's edge one can hear the echoes from the past, for it was here that the drover's trail ran south from Tennessee following the winding course of the French Broad. Herds of cattle, flocks of geese and turkeys passed through this gorge on their way to market in South Carolina.

And every half dozen miles or so along this stretch of river, there was once a tavern or inn where the weary traveler could rest. Almost all of these tavern people were honest men, good hosts, caring for men and cattle alike. But there was one tavern along the river that was not like the rest.

And should you walk today along the banks of the river near the site of this tavern you may still hear the cries of the ghosts of murdered men.

But now let us tell you why this stretch of river will forever be haunted by its past.

The white sarvis trees were in bloom and it was a beautiful day that spring afternoon of 1864 when Clifford Young rode into the little town of Marshall, North Carolina. Surrounded by steep purple mountains, the homes perched precariously on stilts against the side of the cliff.

The traveler had made up his mind that since there were at least two more hours of daylight, he would seek lodging on the drover's road and stopped to question the first villager he met about a place to stay overnight.

"Wall, I reckon you might say Chunn's Tavern is nearest," the mountaineer replied. "That is if you ain't afeard to stay there."

"Afraid? Why should I be?" asked Young curiously.

"Oh, no reason 'cept them that stays there ain't always heered from again—least not in this world. Some folks says the place is haunted."

Young could hardly refrain from smiling at this bit of mountain credulity, and after asking the distance to the "haunted" hostelry he rode on through town. A few minutes later his horse was trotting cautiously along a steep and rugged path. Ordinarily darkness held little fear for this ex-soldier who had lived through the horrors of the Confederate retreat from Nashville. But as night began to close in around him in this densely wooded hill country, he could not shake off a feeling of apprehension.

His eyes strained to see ahead in the fast deepening twilight. Heavy undergrowth fringed the trail at either edge and horse and rider seemed to share a sense of dread as they passed through the gloomy depths of the woods.

A shrill cry shattered the stillness. Young started, then reigned his mare in more tightly just as she stumbled and almost lost her balance. For a moment the animal stood still, gave a nervous whinney and then continued to climb.

He could only conjecture that the cry had been that of some animal, perhaps a wildcat. But try as he would to suppress such thoughts, Young's mind kept returning to the mountaineer's warning. He could not dispel his depression.

It was in this mood that he finally rounded a bend in the trail and saw Chunn's Tavern for the first time. There it stood, a huge monstrosity of a building, crouched with its back against the mountainside. Across its face ran a long, overhanging porch. Dim strips of light showed through the shuttered windows. And beside the front door hung a perforated metal lantern like a malevolent eye emitting sparks of hate.

89

Young's first thought was that the tavern's appearance lent itself well to the mountaineer's tale. But he upbraided himself for such foolishness and, dismounting, lifted the large knocker on the door. It was opened almost immediately by a short, heavyset fellow. And with a hearty familiarity which Young found most repellent, the man ushered him in.

"My name is Chunn and we are so delighted, so delighted to have such a gentleman as yourself stop with us," greeted his host unctuously. Chunn's manner and vacuous looking face filled Young with revulsion, but at least his fears were groundless. Certainly, a man of this sort was far too servile to be dangerous. Such a manner was more often found in cowards.

Chunn introduced him to his wife, a scrawny woman with piercing black eyes who preceded him up the stairs and to his room. As it was seven o'clock, Young decided that he would sup in the main room below and come back up to bed immediately thereafter. Tomorrow's ride would be a long one.

The huge fireplace with its blazing logs radiated warmth and made the dining room of the tavern unexpectedly cheerful. Young forgot his somber thoughts of a short while before and gazed curiously around him at the other lodgers.

His eyes fell first on an overdressed, bumptious pair whom he guessed might be a sutler and his wife. Her bonnet was laden with feathers and furbelows and from beneath its brim stared tiny, gimlet eyes made smaller by the puffy folds of flesh around them. Her trader husband was as grossly corpulent as she. And his face looked as if a huge hand had been stroked downward upon it blurring any traces of character it might once have had.

At another table sat a rough looking fellow who still wore the cape style army overcoat of the Union forces. But Young had a suspicion it had been borrowed without leave from some unlucky Yankee. The man was determined to avoid his eye.

The most sensitive and intelligent face belonged to a young man with a russet beard who sat nearest him. His clothes gave off an air of quiet elegance, a bit startling in this isolated mountain area. At this moment the young man arose and walked over to his table.

"I would guess from your bearing, sir, that you have been a military man. Is that true?"

Replying courteously in the affirmative, Young invited him to join him. His name was Clarkson, and he proved to be a Virginian like himself. One might judge from his dress that he was extremely well-to-do. Young was particularly struck by the heavy gold chain and handsome watch which Clarkson wore.

The two men must have talked for over an hour when they noticed it was getting late and, both wanting to make an early start the following morning, they bid each other the friendliest of good-nights and retired to their own quarters.

As Clifford Young unlocked the door of his room he heard a footstep just behind him. Wheeling around he saw the rough looking fellow he had noticed in the dining room. Still in his army overcoat he scurried past and ducked furtively through a door a short distance down the hall. What was behind the man's strange manner and why had he attempted to avoid his gaze in the dining room?

Young puzzled over it as he lay in his bed leafing through the pages of his Jefferson's Bible. He must have read later than he realized for when he turned down his lamp, it was half after eleven. He had just begun to doze off, comfortable under the warmth of the heavy quilts, when he heard it. His whole body tingled with horror. He heard the sound of a man's screams, screams so fearful that all the dark corners of the mind must have joined hands and forced their way out through a human throat. There was a dull thudding noise and then —silence.

Clifford Young jumped from his bed and as he did so his own lamp flickered out and he found himself in total darkness. For a few seconds he stood tensed, half expecting some intruder to throw himself upon him from the blackness. But nothing happened and finally his fumbling fingers grasped the doorknob. He flung it wide open and there, squarely in front of him, stood Mrs. Chunn, her eyes wide and enigmatic.

"Oh, you are awake, sir. How you did startle me throwing the door open that way."

"Madam, where did that screaming come from?"

"Screaming? I didn't hear anything. Perhaps one of the gentlemen had a nightmare."

As Young started to move past her into the hall, the woman stepped almost imperceptibly to one side so that he found his way blocked. For a moment they stood staring at one another. Then, loath to argue with her, Young turned and went back into his room. But there was no sleep left for him that night.

He arose very early and, dressing quickly, ate breakfast and left Chunn's Tavern. Mist still hung over the mountainside making it hard to see any distance ahead. The sharp turn in the trail was upon him before he realized it as he rode along. He heard a crackling sound in the brush but took it to be a fox or a rabbit. Then and utterly without warning came the sharp report of a gun from his right. Recalling a trick he had used to advantage during the war, Young allowed himself to fall from his horse as though hit and his hand came to rest on his revolver.

The figure of a man emerged from a thicket and as it did so Young drew aim and fired. His assailant fell. Leaping to his feet with his revolver still pointed at the figure on the ground he advanced cautiously. To his amazement, he found what appeared to be the body of a dead Negro man. As he turned him over Young saw something glitter in the half light of the early morning. And out of the dead man's pocket fell a gold watch and chain. It was the watch and chain Clarkson had worn the night before.

Anger swept over him like a torrent and his first thought was to get back to the tavern. He rode with the abandon of a madman and wrenching open the door called out to Mrs. Chunn.

"I have just killed the man who murdered Clarkson. What do you know of all this?"

The woman stood stone still, her face ashen.

"My God!" she screamed. "You have killed my husband!" And with that she ran out of the tavern and up the trail.

For the first time the realization of what had actually happened took shape in Clifford Young's mind. He knew now the fate of the guests at the "tavern of terror." His friend, Clarkson, had died at the hands of the Chunns the night before, and prosperous looking guests who were not done away with at the tavern were waylaid on the trail. Where the trail turned made an ideal place to ambush travelers and Chunn, himself, had lain in wait for him that morning, blackening his face as a disguise and attempting to murder him. This time Alfred Chunn had met his match.

His and his wife's game of death with their hapless lodgers was over forever. But for many years afterwards riders along this isolated mountain road often reported hearing wild cries and seeing eerie figures appear suddenly in front of them. It is not surprising, for if the spirits of those who die a violent death are restless and prone to return, there are many with a reason to haunt this road. And, certainly, the evil spirit most likely to wait and watch and linger on out of the past is the ghost of Alfred Chunn himself.

If you should go this way at night, look for him. He may be looking for you.

The SURRENCY Ghost

It is doubtful whether one person in a thousand driving down Highway 82 through Jessup, Georgia, knows that they are close to the site of one of the strangest supernatural occurrences on record.

Terrifying events took place at the plantation of Millard Surrency despite his reluctance at first to discuss them. From 1872 to 1877, thousands of people visited "Surrency," including scientists bent on explaining away the events and reporters sent from their newspapers to investigate. A railroad even ran special trains for people to watch such predictably regular exhibitions of the supernatural.

One summer afternoon in June of 1872, Mrs. Surrency sat quietly sewing in her bedroom. The beautiful mahogany headboard of the four poster bed gleamed in the light of the sunshine which streamed through the window. Her husband, Millard, was pleased with the stand of cotton on the plantation. The children were enjoying the swimming, dancing and exchange of visits, all part of the pleasures of summer. Mrs. Surrency could not have been happier.

As she sewed a feeling of contentment pervaded her and she didn't notice a noise behind her. It came again and she looked around the room but saw nothing. The third time she realized that it came from the washstand behind her which was near the head of the bed. She stopped her work and gazed at it curiously. To her amazement, the pitcher in the washstand bowl at first almost imperceptibly, then with greater agitation, began to rock back and forth. Gradually enough momentum was generated so that it actually inscribed an arc over the side of the bowl and landed upright beside it on the washstand. Mrs. Surrency was now sure that one of her boys must have tied a string to the pitcher and be playing a trick upon her. She examined the pitcher, but there was no sign of any string.

Ann Surrency was calm of temperament and her first reaction was more that of puzzlement than fear. She had just turned toward the door, wondering where the boys were, when a loud crash came from behind her. Turning she saw the floor in front of the washstand covered with fragments of china and glass. The bowl lay in a thousand fragments at her feet. Pieces of the matching china soap dish were there, too. Even the hand-painted glasses at the back of the stand were now nothing but sharp, silvery slivers among the debris scattered upon the dark floor.

While Mrs. Surrency stood in astonishment gazing at the remains of her once lovely toilet set, she happened to look over at the washstand just as the pitcher began to rise slowly into the air. As if tilted by some invisible hand, it remained poised while the water it contained was poured slowly out upon the rug. Then with a kind of savage flourish it was lifted high and flung to the floor.

Mrs. Surrency ran from the room.

The first person she met was her sixteen-year-old daughter, Clementine, and son, Millard, Jr., who had come into the large center hall. They were calling her to settle an argument as to who was to ride their father's handsome new stallion, Sea Horse, first. Both hushed quickly when they saw the expression on their mother's face.

She told them what had happened and during the conversation their father came in from his morning tour of the plantation. After some discussion everyone tended to think that the entire incident was probably the result of an earthquake tremor. So they dismissed it from their minds.

The next day as the family were together for

A railroad ran special trains for people to watch these strange happenings of the supernatural

their mid-day meal, a door which opened on the long gallery at the side of the house closed with a loud bang. The entire family jumped at the unexpected noise, then agreed that it must have been the wind.

"Perhaps we are going to have a summer storm," said Mr. Surrency, folding his napkin. As he did so the Surrencys heard the same heavy door creak open and close with such a violent crash that it almost shook the house. Young Millard pointed speechless at two of the dining room windows. The two windows which had been raised were now edging downward simultaneously. They struck the sills and began to go back up faster until as they opened and closed loudly several times some of the small panes were shattered.

Clementine began to cry. Her mother tried to sooth her. Young Millard went over to check the windows while Millard Surrency, Sr., and his older brother Robert ran out of the dining room toward the gallery. They could see no one, and a thorough search of the grounds near the home revealed nothing.

Entering the separate kitchen back of the house, Mr. Surrency found the family butler and cook. Both looked extremely frightened. Maggie literally shook, and the pair seemed as puzzled by the racket as the Surrencys.

This was only the beginning. From then on many strange and frightening incidents took place, although they seemed to be restricted to Mrs. Surrency's bedroom or the dining room. On several occasions the family sat down to a beautifully set table and appetizing meal and before there was sufficient time for the family to bow their head for the blessing, the table cloth with the serving dishes, plates, crystal and everything upon it would be snatched from the table. The food was unceremoniously dumped into the Surrency's laps and on the floor.

Even when the Surrency's meals stayed on the table there was a continual succession of other minor, although sometimes painful, disasters. Hot tea, coffee, or soup was often flung in the faces of various members of the family. Their forks or spoons sometimes broke in two or were twisted out of shape even as they held them in their hands.

It was not long before the events, first confined to Mrs. Surrency's bedroom and the dining room, began to spread throughout the house. Doors and windows would slam, furniture would begin to move in an eerie dance about the room, then back to its place, or fall forward with a crash which sometimes shattered valuable family pieces. There was an ever-present danger for the children as heavy wardrobes and bureaus tended to suddenly topple forward, and mirrors and pictures frequently fell from the walls.

These weird phenomena went on during the night as well as the day until the entire family barely ate or slept, awaiting the next shocking event.

For some reason the manifestations seemed to single out young Clementine for the most lurid and dramatic demonstrations. If she touched a table, when she withdrew her hand the table followed her, floating along perhaps a foot above the floor. If she sat in a chair, when she arose the chair would trail her throughout the house. It was a strange sight indeed to watch Clementine Surrency go down the stairs, through the house and out to the garden with a chair floating right along just a few feet behind her.

Even worse, it became so that Clementine could scarcely enter the room without all the furniture lifting from the floor and engaging in a weird, maniacal kind of dance, whirling here and there for as long as five minutes at a time, until suddenly all became still. Or one would crash with incredible ferocity into another, wrecking some beautiful family heirloom.

The Surrencys discussed moving to another plantation which Mr. Surrency owned, but they had spent many happy years in this house built in the 1840's and they were reluctant to leave.

Mrs. Surrency became increasingly alarmed over the physical safety of the children and that of Clementine in particular. Invisible hands would tug her hair roughly, her bedclothes were snatched from the bed. Sometimes as the girl was about to go to sleep, her bed would begin to rock violently to and fro as if attempting to throw her out of it. Early one morning in February, she was lifted entirely out of bed just before the incredibly heavy canopied bed was overturned, falling sideways on the floor with a horrendous crash which awakened the entire household.

That day the family made up their minds that they would move to the other plantation as soon as they could pack their belongings, a matter of a few days. But the move was not destined to be made in so leisurely a fashion. For that very afternoon the danger of the malevolent force at work in the Surrency house showed itself most clearly. As young Sam Surrency walked into the library where his brother Robert sat quietly reading in a chair before the fire, he saw one of the huge brass andirons lift itself from the flames into the air. For a moment it poised itself as if gathering every possible ounce of force. Then the massive andiron hurled itself through the air in the direction of Robert's head who sat unsuspecting in the chair. Before Sam could reach him the andiron had dealt Robert a glancing blow on the head. Sam

94

tried to grasp the andiron but it was wrested from his hands and again struck Robert. This time the boy ran for his life. But the andiron followed, striking him viciously until he fell unconscious to the floor in a pool of blood. The andiron then rose into the air and, moving down the wide center hall, re-entered the library and settled itself back in the fireplace.

That evening the Surrencys, with the help of friends, moved Robert and the rest of the family to the other plantation, closing the old homeplace and taking only their clothes. The other house was furnished also and in addition there was the thought in each one's mind that the old furniture was unwelcome in new surroundings. Robert's wounds became infected and illness followed.

For almost two weeks the emotionally exhausted Surrencys recovered from the habit of jumping at every slight sound, not knowing what would soon follow. Broken limbs, wounds and bruises healed. Many of these latter were suffered by the children who had been caught beneath falling cabinets, wardrobes, et cetera.

But emotional stability had only begun to return when all the nightmarish events descended upon them again. For a few days the family did not talk about it with outsiders, but they soon became desperate. As word of the Surrency ghost spread many distinguished people came to investigate such as Bridges Smith, Mayor of Macon, and Henry Pendleton, Editor of the Macon Telegram. Many reliable people, neighbors who lived near Jessup, Georgia, saw these weird phenomena take place.

Finally, the well-known medium and clairvoyant of the day, Foster, visited the Surrency home with some of his friends and remained for a week investigating. He reported that he had been in contact with spirits who told him the entire Surrency family was strongly mediumistic, especially Clementine. These were the type of people, said Foster, which spirits sought out to convey their messages to others. The Surrency family took little stock in Foster's explanation.

Shortly after their troubles began in their new home, Millard Surrency started building a small house on another piece of property he owned. When they were ready to move, he gave in to Clementine's pleadings to visit their old home so that she might pack up some of her belongings which she had left in the family's hasty move.

While Clementine packed her trunk in the house her father walked around looking at the grounds once more. Soon Clementine returned telling him her trunk was ready to be brought down. Even as she spoke there came the sound of crashing glass. The trunk hurtled through the closed window and shutters and fell on the lawn near them. The lid had burst open and the girl's clothes, in wild disarray, were spilling over the side and out on the lawn. And they were literally torn to shreds.

"We mustn't ever come here again," cried Clementine. She clung to her father sobbing hysterically.

"This house must certainly be cursed by some unspeakable evil," said Surrency. And from that day on none of the Surrency family ever returned. For over 45 years the house sat deserted until it finally burned.

The problems of the family ended after they moved into their new home which founded the small community of Surrency, Georgia. But the frightening phenomena which had plagued the family for so long were never solved and for years the people of nearby Jessup, who had actually seen the weird events taking place, continued to talk of them. Many had been eye witnesses to incidents which so completely violated human understanding they could only conjecture a force was at work which was in no way bound by natural laws. And to this day the ghost of Surrency has never been explained.

The
KING'S MESSENGERS

*On rainy nights the eerie pair
still roam, galloping along
forever carrying a message
never to be delivered*

Major Ferguson leaned back against the white oak tree and reflected upon his situation.

His proclamation for the mountain men to surrender may have been flamboyant, but he never really expected it to create this kind of reaction. Hundreds of men were appearing as if by magic from over the mountains, traveling under the command of Campbell, Shelby, Sevier and others from that almost mythical land beyond Quaker Meadows, even beyond the edge of his map. They were coming to do battle with him. They were coming down to the lowlands to fight for their independence and there was an understanding among them that they would not go home until either they or Ferguson had been defeated.

For several days now he had been sending out his messengers in pairs, two by two, to alert Lord Cornwallis at his headquarters in Charlottesburg as to the situation. Not that his position on King's Mountain was that precarious, but he wouldn't have minded a regiment of the king's dragoons close enough to support him.

Ordinarily Major Ferguson was not the kind of man to worry, but somehow messengers were not getting through to Lord Cornwallis and in the cold chill of the October wind, he sensed the hostility of these backwoods people who refused to bow to the British flag or—what was more important—pay taxes.

The day before he had sent some of his best riders off but still there was no return message from Lord Cornwallis. No need to waste any more of his good men on futile errands. Tonight he would send a couple of the Tory militia. He would select natives of the area, roughly dressed. They certainly would not get lost and if they ran into any mountain men, they'd be instant turncoats for as long as it took to get off down the road.

James and Douglas Duncan were farm born and bred. Unlettered but fairly shrewd fellows, their greatest loyalty was to their possessions and the protection the British flag might give their land.

Ferguson summoned the two brothers and gave them this most vital message instructing them to deliver it in person to Lord Rawdon or Lord Cornwallis at Charlottesburg. He warned them about the hazards of their mission, told them of the messengers who had not gotten through, cautioned them to talk to no one and then dispatched the nondescript pair on horseback.

For some time they rode along on this cold, rainy October night, meeting neither friend nor foe. After they had galloped for a number of miles without incident, they reached the South

Fork of the Catawba River. They plunged the animals into the stream and with a great splashing and whinneying they forded the river. The men were relieved to find a tavern there at which to refresh themselves.

The tavern mistress had just lost her husband at the battle of Camden and the two sympathized with her volubly. So much so that she generously made their drinks extra hearty and as their tongues loosened, their braggadoccio remarks began to arouse the woman's suspicions that here were two Tories bent on mischief of some kind. Seeing they were almost ready to leave she slipped out of the room and up to the attic of the tavern where she stood by the window waiting. Their horses were tethered just below her and she knew the direction they would ride in. She had just taken out a brace of pistols when the two drunken couriers appeared below her, mounted their horses and rode off. Taking aim she fired the first shot at the one on the right. Nothing happened. The other pistol fired a second later at the rider on the left. But neither man fell and the two riders galloped on, disappearing down the muddy road and into the night.

It was nearing four o'clock in the morning when innkeeper Amos Bissell near Salisbury heard a rough pounding at the door and, awakening, looked down to see what guests could be arriving at this hour on such a cold and rainy night. It was pitch black and, unable to see anyone, all he could hear was what appeared to be the loud voices of two men raised in anger.

"We should have taken a path toward the east hours ago. You don't know the way after all, you simpleton!"

"This is the way that varmint of a woman said to go."

"Well, drat her miserable Whig soul. Her advice is as worthless as the Continental Congress."

The two men lit a lantern and brought out a large map which they spread upon a tree stump. Now the innkeeper could see their horses. One man held the lantern while the other appeared to be studying it.

"We'd better ask the way again. Charlottesburg can't be fur from here," Bissell heard one of the men say.

He threw a long coat on over his nightshirt and unlocking the door to his room, picked his way carefully down the steep curving staircase, candle in hand. He stopped to pick up a flintlock pistol, just as a precaution, and began to walk carefully around the sleeping forms of his guests who lay stretched out on the floor around the fireplace.

Slipping back the heavy iron bolt on the Inn door he peered out. There was no one there. Drawing the coat more tightly around him, he ventured a few feet from the Inn, and then around the corner of the building growing increasingly curious, but he still saw nothing at all nor did he hear even the slightest sound. The rain had stopped but the ground was soft and soggy. Going over to the large tree stump where he had seen the two men spread out the map, Bissell scrutinized the ground around it thoroughly looking for prints of boots and horses' hooves. But not only was the yard of the Inn deserted, there was not a mark to be found. A strange chill began at the back of Amos Bissell's neck and traveled the length of his spine. He was just as frightened as he could be and he scurried quickly back into the Inn, bolted the front door and leaned his back against it. His heart was beating so rapidly he rested there a moment until he could compose himself.

Nor was this the last time the two riders were seen. Travelers on the road between Salisbury and Charlotte often saw the riders. Sometimes they were traveling away from their destination. One stagecoach driver said he had "given them directions so many times that he was beginning to resent the delays every time he met them."

Particularly wherever the road forked, the forms of the two couriers were often seen huddled together looking at their map to decide which fork to take. And anyone who chanced by was always hailed and asked the way to Charlottesburg.

"We must be there by morning," one of the men would invariably say.

Drivers of the stagecoaches found that their horses became fidgety and nervous when approaching the riders, as if they sensed the two shadowy figures no longer belonged to the natural world.

So, as time went on and the war was finally won and the last British soldiers departed for their homeland, the king's messengers became couriers without an army. On rainy nights the eerie pair still roamed, galloping along forever with a message never to be delivered, the writer of the message long since dead and buried in the red earth of King's Mountain.

Settlements grew into towns, then cities, and the two riders became wary of the main roads, taking to the country lanes in their endless search for the way to Charlottesburg.

Some say you can still see them. A cold, rainy night in early October is the best time to look for the King's Messengers. For then they are most apt to suddenly appear galloping over the hill on some lonely dirt road between King's Mountain and Salisbury, two specters hurtling through the night on their phantom steeds, pausing sporadically to inquire the way to Charlottesburg. And, if by chance they should ask you, it doesn't really matter in which direction you point for even with the best of directions an invisible power thwarts and diverts the restless apparitions at every turn.

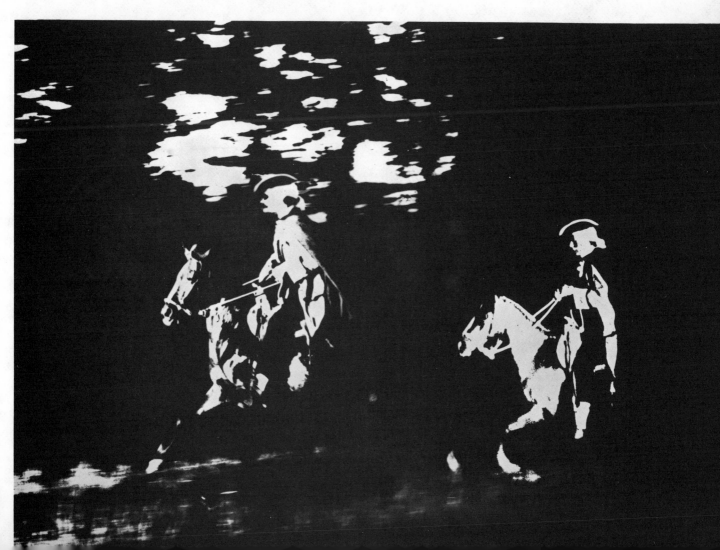

The HAUNTED GOLD MINE

The Carolina Gold Rush could have made him the richest man in the world until a ghost stepped in

They called him "Skinflint" MacIntosh and said if you happened to pass him sideways you couldn't see him. It was kind of a local joke in every country store between Charlotte and Concord that the only way you could see MacIntosh was from the front or back.

Not only skinny in size, he also happened to be skinny when it came to generosity, or at least that's what everyone said. But the old man was not concerned over what was said about him at the country stores or jokes about his appearance, for he owned the richest hill of gold between the Reed Mine* and the United States Mint at Charlotte.

It may have looked like just another field of red clay on top but when MacIntosh got the report that the vein of gold 450 feet down was four feet wide, it brought the only kind of joy a mind like his could truly appreciate.

Of course, there was a problem. Even with the shaft dug he must persuade enough men to go down that far and dig in the damp darkness beneath the surface of the earth and haul out his treasure. There were plenty of fellows to be had for placer mining on the surface. This needed men with more skill and more courage.

* Roberts, Bruce, *The Carolina Gold Rush*, McNally and Loftin, 510 W. 4th St., Charlotte, N. C. 1971.

But Mr. MacIntosh was unworried. He knew how to do it. He sat on his hill and looked at the broomstraw, a warm, rusty color in the glow of the setting sun. He picked up a lump of red clay, pressing and shaping it between his fingers, and he could picture shovel after shovel full of that red clay turning to pure gold!

It seemed hard to believe that he had been picked, perhaps, he thought, by God himself, to become the richest man in North Carolina. Why, someday people would still be talking about the gold that came out of his mine long after they had forgotten mines like the Dixie Queen, the New Nugget and the Yellow Dog. What if the Reed Mine had been the first mine in this country to gain fame and start the Carolina gold rush, his mine would outproduce them all!

The next morning Mr. MacIntosh went to the store at Georgeville where he knew he would find not only some experienced miners from the Reed Mine but also newly arrived young men who had flocked into the area eager to make their fortunes. Standing there resting one hand on the counter and smiling his friendliest smile, Mr. MacIntosh announced he would pay half again whatever the other mine operators were paying.

"You'll have to," said Joe McGee sitting back with his chair tilted against the counter. "Who wants to go that far down to dig? No amount a' money is worth workin' for if a man don't come up at the end of the day to collect." There was a sizzling sound as he spat at the stove.

For a moment MacIntosh sensed that something could go wrong. There was his fortune and he

was willing to pay high wages for men to dig it up for him but somehow these men were not jumping at his offer. Was his mine any different from the others? He alone knew it was the richest. The hairs rose along the back of his neck and for no longer than it takes a snake to flick its tongue, MacIntosh felt cold enough to shiver. There was even a flash of foreboding, but it didn't last long.

"Come up at the end of the day to collect. What are you talkin' about, Joe? It don't matter how deep a mine is. Whether it's two hundred or three hundred feet under the ground. You just brace the roofs of those tunnels up with good, hefty timber and you dig out the gold the same way. I've been down in that mine myself many a time and I've got the finest oak timbers and braces money can buy."

Mr. MacIntosh knew that was a lie even as he said it. But he smiled his biggest smile again and said, "All right, men, sign up over here, all of you who want to go to work for me Monday morning and start getting rich."

Joe McGee leaned back against the counter and said, "Mr. MacIntosh, if you got the safest mine like you say you have, and I got no reason to doubt you, then there's no danger workin' in your mine."

"That's right," replied MacIntosh. "Why, you're just about as safe down there as a man could be."

"All right," said Joe. "I'll come to work for you."

Everyone was surprised because they knew that Joe was probably the best foreman at the Reed Mine and he knew the mining business well.

"But, Mr. MacIntosh, there's just one thing. You wouldn't mind paying my wife a thousand dollars if I did happen to get buried down there in your mine, would you?"

"Joe, I wouldn't pay your wife just one thousand dollars. I'd pay her two thousand!"

102

Well, that did it. Two thousand dollars was more money than most of the men had ever seen. Joe quit the Reed Mine that afternoon and told the boss he was leaving to work for MacIntosh. At least a dozen other men did the same thing because on the following Monday there was almost a full crew ready to go down into the MacIntosh Mine.

Soon large quantities of ore were being brought up and MacIntosh's excitement was so great these first few weeks that he even treated some of the men to a free drink in the local saloon.

The yield per ton of pure gold, after the Chilean mill had done its work, was incredibly high, it was said, but MacIntosh never told anyone exactly what the yield per ton was. Some of the men were finding sizeable gold nuggets. But most of the gold was found in fissure veins of quartz. This quartz was seldom glassy but rather milky white in color and often stained brown.

On his first payday Joe bought his wife a pair of fine silk stockings. She still worried about him and at first he had to reassure her almost daily. Finally, when he had told her how safe the mine was, he would laugh and with his blue-green eyes dancing mischievously, remind her that, "Why, if anything did happen to me you'd be rich, lassie! Old MacIntosh promised me himself that you would get two thousand dollars."

So, as the weeks passed and Joe returned safely each night to the little house where his wife, and then a baby as well, awaited him, her fears eased.

But, on the evening of the winter's first snowfall, Joe did not come home at the accustomed time. It had been a cold, gray, drizzly afternoon with the fine rain turning into snow and Jennie's spirits were low. But she counted this due to the weather remembering that sometimes on a cold day, Joe would stop off with his friend Shaun O'Hennessy and buy a drink, so she refused to worry.

However, by nine o'clock she was quite alarmed. Wrapping the baby warmly, she left the infant with her neighbor and set out toward the saloon. She saw lights inside, laughter drifted out into the snow-flecked blackness and when she opened the door she was engulfed in the warm air, tobacco smoke and voices.

Tommy McSwain, the owner, walked over to her immediately. "What can I do for you, Jennie McGee?" But he was unable to answer any questions about Joe.

"No, mam. Last time Joe was in here was three nights ago. Seems like he and Shaun came in after work. Yes, that's the way it was."

"Anybody seen Joe McGee?" he called out to the men, a number of whom were looking curiously at Jennie by now, for it was plain to see she was upset.

There was a chorus of no's and Jennie left, deciding she would walk on beyond the saloon to Shaun O'Hennessy's. Mary opened the door and she could see Shaun dozing before the fire. He got up stiffly from his chair when he heard the door close behind her.

"What are you doing out at this time of night, my girl? Where is Joe? I waited for him this afternoon, but he said he was going to work awhile longer so I came on home. This back of mine's been hurtin' somethin' terrible."

"Jennie, what's wrong with you," said Shaun's wife, Mary.

Tears streamed down Jennie's face but at first there was no sound. Then she flung herself into Mary's arms weeping and screaming.

"He's still down there. I know he is. He's had an accident or he'd be home by now. Get him out, Shaun, get him out! *Please!* Go down to the mine tonight."

"Mary, take her home and stay with her until I come and pick you up."

O'Hennessy pulled on his still wet boots which sat beside the fire, reached for his coat and hat which hung on a wooden peg near the door, and left.

Near the saloon he met Big Pete and they rounded up several other men to join them. The mine was only a little over a mile away but the snow made walking more treacherous and the little knot of silent miners tramped along through the blackness punctuated here and there by pinpoints of light from miners' cabins.

Three men passed, arms linked, singing a bawdy song at the top of their lungs. The one nearest Shaun jostled him roughly and if it had been any other time he would have regretted it for Shaun's Irish temper would certainly have blazed up. But his face grew just a shade more grim and he pressed on, ignoring the fellow.

It was cold and raw and the road underfoot which led up the hill to the mine was muddy. But there were stars out and it had begun to clear. The men trudged on, their heavy boots making a scrunching sound on the pieces of quartz and dark greenish gray rocks which lay along the roadbed.

Finally, they reached the place where the mine shaft lay and Shaun and one of the other men, each with their lanterns, started down the ladder and, with the light from the lanterns flickering on the sides of the shaft hewed deep into the red clay, down, down they went, past the gaping holes of old tunnels worked in bygone years and on to the vein the men were working now.

The two men walked the full length of the tunnel where they had worked that day and for

the past several months. They called and then they listened. But there was no sound save the muffled echo of their own voices and the scraping of their boots on granite-like rock. After they had searched fruitlessly for about an hour they went back up to the surface where the small huddle of miners who had accompanied them waited.

The next day Jennie went to MacIntosh's office still certain that Joe was somewhere within the mine and asked him to send a search party to comb some of the lesser worked tunnels. Four of the men including Shaun accompanied her, but MacIntosh pooh-poohed the plan and said Joe would show up again "when he gets good and ready." Two weeks passed and still there was no sign of Joe so Jennie, convinced of Joe's devotion to her, was certain by now that he was dead. She visited MacIntosh again, this time to make claim for the two thousand dollars he had promised to pay if Joe were killed in the mine. MacIntosh suggested this time that perhaps Joe had not been so happy with married life, but to wait awhile longer. By now, Jennie and the baby were low on food and firewood and the other miners and their wives were taking by whatever food they could to share and Shaun O'Hennessy was chopping firewood for his own family and Jennie as well.

The next time Jennie went to the mine office MacIntosh sent a message out that he did not have time to see her. In tears she stopped by the O'Hennessy shack on her way home and Mary O'Hennessy made her stay on for some hot stew. Over and over she kept moaning, "He's dead, he's dead. He's down there somewhere dead. What will the baby and I do now."

That night it had barely struck twelve when there came a terrible rattling sound at the O'Hennessy door. Shaun pulled on his trousers and stumbled toward it sleepily. Without thinking he threw the door wide open and then he wished he had not, for before him stood the most frightful

104

figure he had ever seen. The cheeks were a waxy chalk white. The eyes in their dark caverns looked like murky red marbles. Gaunt, clothes encrusted all over with dirt, one could hardly tell that it was a man.

Shaun covered his eyes in horror. A voice spoke.

"Ah, Shaun O'Hennessy. You were the best friend I had in all the world, and now you will not even look on me. Are you going to leave me down in the dark and the damp of the mine forever? And what about Jennie? Is old 'Skinflint' going to pay her the money for my life? What about your Mary? And the rest of the wives. Do you ken he will do any the better by them? Look at me, Shaun."

O'Hennessy lowered his arm slowly from before his eyes and peered at the specter of his old friend. For this weird spirit in front of him had once been Joe McGee.

"I heard you the night you came to look for me, Shaun, but you went down too deep. Stop at the second tunnel and go in. If you'll walk far enough, you'll find me. That's where I decided to stop and work for awhile the day I didn't go out with you. I was striking rich ore when the timber gave way and buried me. But none of that matters now. Has MacIntosh given Jennie any money?"

"No, he won't give it to her, Joe."

"Won't give it to her! Well, blast him! Why not?"

"Says you ain't dead, Joe. Just went off and left her."

The ghost flew into a terrible rage and as brave a man as he was, Shaun O'Hennessy began to tremble.

"The liar! The greedy old devil! I'll haunt that mine of his forever," shouted the specter. Then he began to calm down somewhat when he saw the effect all this was having on his friend.

"Now, Shaun. You ain't scared of your old buddy Joe, are you? I want you to get Big Pete, Casey, Henry and Sam and come after me."

"Yeah, yeah. Tomorrow morning. We'll be there, Joe."

"No, not tomorrow morning. Tonight!" And with that the ghost vanished.

Still shaking, Shaun pulled on his boots and left. He knew he was not going down into that mine alone. He made four stops and each miner came with him after he told them about seeing Joe's ghost. Tonight there was moonlight and it seemed to Shaun that they reached the mine quickly, almost too quickly. The men were jumpy and uneasy but they were determined to find out if the specter had really been the ghost of Joe McGee. Single file they went down the ladder.

Casey walked along in front of the others watching for holes in the floor of the tunnel or loose overhead timbers. They had walked for perhaps two hundred feet when a voice spoke up and said, "I've been waiting for you, boys," and there stood the specter, white-faced, hollow-eyed and clothes encrusted with dirt.

"It's time you knew old MacIntosh is one of the worst liars there ever was. This mine ain't safe and it never will be because them's cheap timbers and a lot of 'em are even rotten. I'm goin' to haunt this mine forever!"

The miners looked terrified but Shaun and Big Pete stood their ground behind Sam and Casey.

"Dig here?" asked Casey.

"Yes," replied the ghost, pointing toward the cave-in. "Why, I've walked all over this mine lately, watchin' you fellows, fearin' for you."

The frightened men dug for almost ten minutes. They were beginning to grow discouraged when there was a ring as Big Pete's shovel struck metal.

The metal turned out to be a pick and the handle of the pick was clutched fast in a man's fist. Shaun and Big Pete dropped their shovels and began to dig with their hands now. Within minutes they had uncovered the body of a man and the man was Joe McGee. No one thought to notice when the ghost disappeared because no one had really wanted to keep looking at it.

They carried Joe's body up on the elevator and home, and the next morning Shaun went to get MacIntosh. He told him Joe McGee was home and "needed to see him and he'd better come."

Mr. MacIntosh looked pretty startled, like he was going to call Shaun down, but instead he decided to go with him. Neither man did any talking on the walk from the mine office over to the McGee shack. There was a crowd of miners standing around outside the little house looking sullen and silent. Three women were standing on the porch talking and MacIntosh made his way through several more who were gathered just outside the front door.

Shaun held the door open and Mr. MacIntosh walked in. At one end of the room was a long pine box and MacIntosh knew even before he walked over to it that Joe McGee lay inside the crude coffin. Jennie sat in the small rocker next to it holding the baby and crying quietly. She did not look up at MacIntosh.

"A thousand dollars, that's what it was, wasn't it," said MacIntosh. Jennie didn't answer.

An angry murmur rose from the men.

"Two thousand," broke in Big Pete. "You know what it is. We was there in the store the day you hired him. We know how often Jennie's been to you to get it."

MacIntosh started toward the door and the men gradually closed the way in front of him until he found himself looking up into the angry face of Pete Petroni whom everybody knew was not called "Big Pete" for nothing. He tried to go around him. "Big Pete" moved blocking his exit.

"All right, two thousand," he said gruffly. "She can pick it up at the mine office."

That afternoon Mary O'Hennessy went with Jennie to pick up her money and it was paid.

But the men did not go back to work that day, nor did they go back the next. Skinflint called an "important meeting" of all the miners. They all came and listened. He promised more money, he bragged about the safety of the mine and he said he had just forgotten how much Joe's wife was to get and that he was so sorry about it he had even given her fifty dollars more.

The men heard him out, their faces impassive. Then they got up and left. But the next morning there was still no sign of life at the mine and he learned that all of the men, except for a few who were packing to leave the area, had hired on at other nearby mines. Word had spread quickly that the MacIntosh mine was haunted, that it always would be, and when that kind of news gets out a mine operator is finished.

For several days MacIntosh visited some of the leaders among the men trying to convince them to go back but they wouldn't even talk with him. Finally, he gave up.

A few weeks later he walked up the hill and began to wander around aimlessly. He looked regretfully at the tall rock smelting furnace from which no smoke had come for days. He sat down at the edge of the huge grinding stones and sifted crushed quartz aimlessly through his fingers as if in a daze.

He had sat this way for perhaps an hour when a mounting fury began to overtake him. His dream of a lifetime was to be destroyed because of some superstitious miners. There was millions of dollars of gold in this hill, but he was never going to see it. He knew it. Somehow there must be a way to get it out.

And then, like an animal gone mad and with tears of frustration streaming down his face, he began to claw at the red clay with his fingers. MacIntosh was not the first man to lose his mind over gold.

A hundred years later the gold is still there. The miners have all left and no one would know that beneath the red clay of these Carolina hills the best and the worst in man struggled with each other in the search for gold.

If you should walk across these hills, you may still hear the wind whispering the names of these mines—the Dixie Queen, the Yellow Dog, the Blue Hill, The Dutch Bend and the Reed Mine, but even the wind does not mention the name of the MacIntosh Mine.

This abandoned safe at Gold Hill is one of the few things left from the Carolina Gold Rush era. It has held many a bag of gold dust.

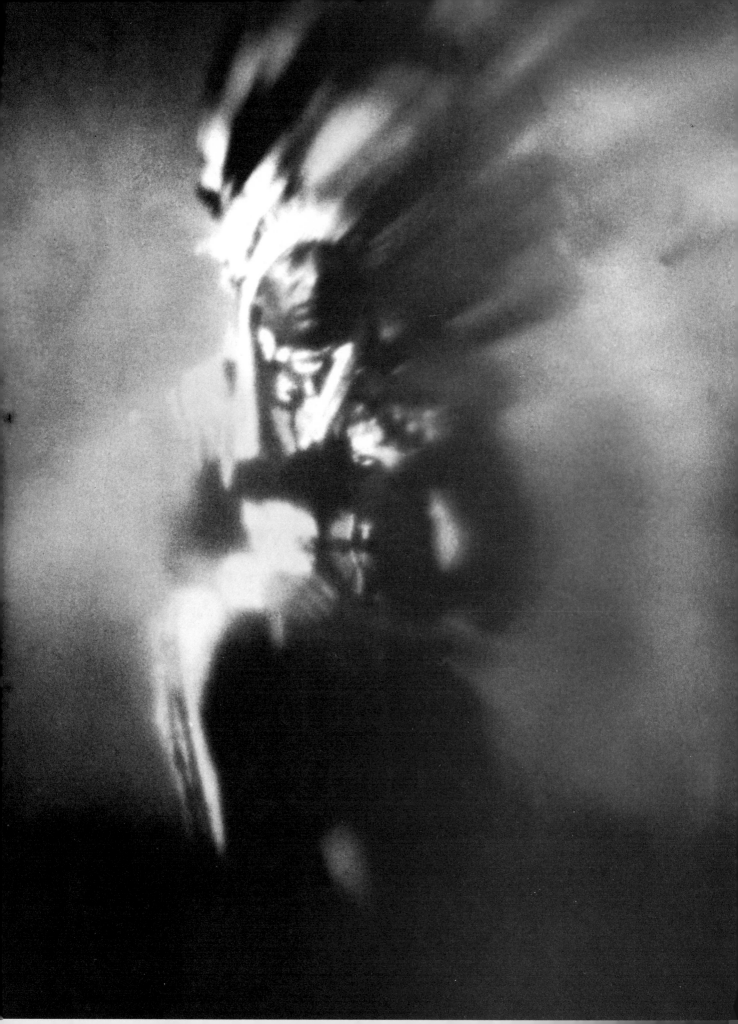

The
SINGING RIVER

*Is it possible that there are lost Indian tribes
who went to live beneath the water?*

Late summer and autumn are the times when the mysterious music of the Pascagoula River is heard most often, and those who have listened to it remember it forever. Some say it is a soft humming sound, others hear the strains of music so beautiful that it is unearthly. Those who have heard it most clearly have been out in a boat on the river itself rather than the bank and have heard the strains of the music begin gently around them and then swell louder and louder. They were caught up and carried along by the power and beauty of the strange melody which yet contained a prevailing note of sadness.

Located on U. S. 90 between Biloxi, Mississippi and Mobile, Alabama, the river is named for the Pascagoula Indians who lived along its banks, and for many years a variety of legends has attempted to explain the music.

One of the best known of these legends is the story of the romance between Princess Anola who was betrothed to the chieftain of the warlike Biloxi Indians and young Altama, son of the Pas-

cagoula chief. The tribe of the Pascagoula was known for their friendly, peaceful ways and unlike some of the other Indian tribes, war never became a pastime with them. Although not as warlike as some, they did not escape that desire for vengeance which started so many Indian wars and even destroyed entire tribes.

The Pascagoulas held their feasts, their rhythmic dances, their burial ceremonies as did all the Indians but for the most part they were content to cultivate the ground with their primitive hooked wooden sticks, planting corn and beans and living in relative peace with their neighbors.

War was far from the minds of Anola and Altama when they first came upon each other in the forest near the Pascagoula village. Altama was quietly fishing in the river when he first heard something more than the normal sound of the water. It was the voice of a girl singing softly and blending with the noises of the forest and stream.

Altama searched the woods all around him but

109

could find no one. Then he gazed up through the branches of the tree right over his head and there, perched among the highest limbs, was a lovely girl. He beckoned to her to come down and the two spent the balance of the afternoon sharing each other's thoughts and dreams. It was the first of many meetings and Altama soon convinced the girl to marry him.

So, one day she left the village of her father and was welcomed warmly by the people of Altama who immediately began to busy themselves preparing the elaborate wedding feast ordered by Altama's father. On the afternoon before the day of the feast a lone Pascagoula brave was out hunting some distance from the village when he heard the sound of voices talking in the Biloxi tongue. He concealed himself well and stood watching while hosts of Biloxi braves in war regalia stole quietly past him traveling in the direction of the Pascagoula village. It was not hard for the hunter to guess that their objective was vengeance upon the Pascagoula for the loss of their angry chieftain's betrothed.

The hunter returned speedily to his tribe with news of the impending disaster, for those whom the Biloxi did not kill, they would surely take as slaves. Altama volunteered to go out alone to meet the Biloxi and offer himself to them in an attempt to save the village, but the other braves would not allow him to do this.

Soon the scout they had sent out to confirm the hunter's story returned. He brought news of many Biloxi warriors on the march, far outnumbering the Pascagoula braves, warriors who would soon descend with warlike screams and cries upon the villagers. A brief council was held and the people chose between death and slavery at the hands of the Biloxi or another alternative—the waters of their beloved river. They made their decision and gathering along the banks the old people and children began to walk out into the dark stream. They were followed by the braves chanting a death song and behind them walked Altama and Anola who embraced and then plunged beneath the swift flowing waters.

When the Biloxi arrived they found burning campfires and preparations for an elaborate wedding feast. But all was deathly still, nor was there any sign of man, woman or child anywhere about. It was a strange scene and there was something so eerie about it that even seasoned warriors found themselves tiptoeing about, looking in the doorways of the small cabins, staring at the smoking meat and warm vessels of food suspiciously if not fearfully. After making certain no one was there, they left, much mystified.

From that day on stories have been told of the "singing river," and of the people who chose death rather than slavery. The rippling, poignant song of the river has been heard down through the years and continues to puzzle those who seek to explain everything by the laws of science.

Interestingly enough, this is only one of a number of Indian stories of strange sounds coming from rivers and other bodies of water. The white man dreams of lost cities which continue to exist below the water and the Indian appears to have dreams buried deep in his memory of lost tribes and warriors who went to live beneath the water. Many of their stories mention songs of sadness or revelry still heard by those who are fortunate and perceptive enough.

As modern man considers building cities on the ocean floor one sometimes wonders whether in the dawn of mankind men were able to live underwater as well as on land and whether these legends dredged up from the dim recesses of men's minds are really remnants of his prehistoric past.

In any event, if you visit the Pascagoula River in the late summer or autumn you may be one of those who will hear the weird and plaintive song of the water, and then you can decide what it is and why it is there.

The GRAY Lady

She walks across the barriers of time to warn the living

Few there are who have not heard the story of the Gray Man of Pawley's Island, South Carolina. He walks the sandy strand of that island to warn inhabitants of impending hurricanes.

But less known is the story of another South Carolina ghost called the Gray Lady and that is a shame. For she walks not on the sands of the shore but from out of the mist of history at the edge of men's minds. She walks as does the Gray Man to carry a warning from the dead to the living, a warning of impending danger and the possibility of assistance.

She first appeared to save the life of her brother, bringing the garments of a monk which enabled him to disguise himself and escape the St. Bartholomew's Day massacre. That was in France four hundred years ago and from time to time after that she appeared to descendants or intimates of the De Saurin family.

It is strange that such an old ghost should appear so young to those who see her. That a ghost could be both beautiful and frightening at the same time is not only possible—it is, it has been and it may be again for there is no proof that she has left South Carolina.

Nina Beaumont knew little about the De Saurin family in Camden when Raoul De Saurin, whom she had consented to marry, invited her there almost a century ago. It was Halloween and a gay party was assembled in one of the beautifully furnished rooms of "Lausanne," the name the family had given to their home. Among the paintings of her future husband's ancestors was one of a lovely girl in the garb of a nun. The face was infinitely sad and somehow Nina's gaze kept returning to it. She began to question Raoul about the nun and his reluctance to talk about her was soon apparent.

"It is such a wild and rainy night outside and so cheerful in this room that I want only to talk about happy things," said Raoul gently.

But this just aroused Nina's curiosity further and other members of the party joined in, begging him to tell the story. Finally, he consented.

"The name of the girl was Eloise De Saurin and she had been confined to a convent by her father to prevent her from marrying a young man who was not of her faith. The convent where he placed her was one of the most severe of the day and after she had spent only a year there Eloise died. Her death was followed shortly afterwards by that of her grieving mother. The father, Darce De Saurin, in a moment of guilt and despair, took his own life. His two sons whom he had banished because of their Protestant sympathies were summoned and arrived in time to hear his confession. He claimed that he had seen Eloise herself and his belief that she had come to reproach him led him to stab

111

himself with the same dagger with which he had threatened the life of the young man she loved."

"The story goes that later she appeared to the brothers, who recognized her instantly, and she left the garments in which my namesake, Raoul, was to escape being massacred. Jules did not escape and was murdered."

"So," said Raoul, "her appearances, according to family tradition, have happened each time before some tragic event in our family. She has always been seen by some member of the family and with the same expression of sorrow. But so far she has not deigned to visit any of us," he said, smiling and making light of the whole story.

Nina, however, could not smile for her good spirits had fled and she felt both depressed and apprehensive. After the guests left she and Raoul stayed to talk awhile longer. Then she went up to her room. Try as she would to go to sleep, she could not, so, throwing on a robe, she decided to go down the hall and see if Raoul's sister was still awake. She took the candle holder from her bedside table and started down the dark hall which was illuminated dimly by the moonlight coming in the window at the end of the hall.

The hall was quite dark but she was able to make out the figure of a woman only a few feet ahead of her. Thinking it was Lucia, Nina called out gaily. But there was no response. The gray-clad figure continued on its way down the hall just in front of her and now, she noticed that rather than walk, it appeared to glide! Who was this strange woman? Her diaphanous robes and shimmering veil lent a supernatural effect both frightening and intriguing. Nina was almost upon her when the woman turned and looked directly at her. The face was young and lovely but filled with sadness. To her amazement she recognized the features as those of the nun in the painting.

The nun gazed at her with tears streaming down her face and clasped her hands as if imploring her for help. Before she could recover herself enough to know what to do, the veiled figure began to

grow dim and melted away like a cloud blown before the wind. Afterwards Nina could not remember whether her candle had blown out or how she had gotten back to her room.

She awoke to find herself still in her robe lying across the bed. And although it was a bright and beautiful day she was filled with foreboding. The face of the nun was etched sharply and clearly upon her consciousness and even if she was unable to understand the events of the night, she felt that it had been a warning, if not for her, for someone she loved. At breakfast she ate little and when Raoul began to talk about the hunt planned for that day she became very upset and begged him not to go. Finally, she told him why and he began to laugh, surprised that she could be so superstitious as to believe in an old legend. Between his affectionate reassurances and some teasing, he quieted her fears so that she waved and managed to smile at him as he rode off to hunt with his friends.

But as the day wore on she found herself restless and extremely uneasy. She was unable to enjoy the company of the other guests or even to read. Nothing could allay the nameless fears which her encounter with the nun had caused.

The hunters failed to return at the expected time that evening and not until dusk was fast settling in among the trees was the thud of horses' hooves heard. Nina and Lucia arrived first to meet the hunters. They both noticed that one of the horses was riderless but when the animal came up they were shocked to see that it carried a limp burden upon its back. It was the horse which belonged to Raoul and the animal carried the lifeless body of his master. Raoul had been shot and killed by a friend in a hunting accident.

The Court Inn at Camden, South Carolina where the Gray Lady was last seen is no longer standing.

112

The story of Nina's experience and her fiance's tragic death was recorded in a family diary and found many years later in an old desk after the De Saurin home had been sold. Even when the huge house became the Court Inn strange stories were told about the place. One of them concerns a school teacher named Lula Tedder.

After her mother had called to tell her that her father was critically ill, Miss Tedder left Savannah, Georgia to drive to her home in North Carolina. It was a rainy, foggy day to drive and the coming of darkness made her decide to spend the night at Camden, South Carolina. She remembered the huge old Inn there where she had stayed many years before with her parents.

The Court Inn, that was the name of it. Now, where had the man at the filling station said it would be? Mill and Laurens Streets, that was the address. And there it stood, shrouded in fog and rain. The big square white building with its high steps leading up to the wide veranda was just as she remembered it.

The rain fell in torrents blown by occasional wild gusts which wrenched and tore at the trees. But from within the Inn lights glowed dimly and she could not recall when she had felt so grateful for shelter of any kind.

Lula did not wonder at the fact that the lobby was empty as she walked across the dark red carpet with its old fashioned floral design. However, her eye was caught by a movement at the far rear of the lobby and she was just in time to catch a glimpse of the graceful figure of a young Catholic nun disappearing through a door. Faintly curious she glanced down at the ledger which served as a register and saw three or four other names, but none with the title Sister before it.

A gray-haired bellboy who must have been as ancient as the Inn itself showed her to a large, comfortable room and she decided to ask him if there were any sisters staying at the Inn that night. Tired as she was she felt a vague loneliness and thought a nun might prove good company.

"No, mam. We got no nuns around here," said the old fellow shaking his head vehemently.

"Now, just let me light that fire for you. The way that wind's a blowin' and a wailin' out there 'mongst them trees, we're goin' to have hurricane weather for sure, and you'll be mighty glad to have that fire."

Lula agreed and for awhile was considerably cheered by the orange flames licking hungrily at the resin rich logs of yellow pine. But the wood burned quickly and as the flames sank lower, the shadows in the corners of the room deepened. She became conscious of an acrid, musty odor and the damp chill of the night air began to seep in around her. Although she resolutely tried to ignore it, Lula was having some very peculiar sensations. No matter how hard she tried not to watch the shadows in the corners of the room, particularly the corner near the front window, her eyes kept coming back to it. As the fire grew lower the shadows seemed to leap even more frenetically. She convinced herself that the mirror over the large oak dresser was reflecting some of the flames, distorting them and causing the strange-looking shadows. So, feeling more like herself, she folded her clothes on a chair and went to bed. Lula was almost asleep when she became aware of a soft, rustling sound coming from the corner near the front window. She started up quickly and over in the corner saw the shadowy figure of a young woman.

"Who is there? Tell me who you are," Lula cried out. The woman wore gray garments and they were the habit of a nun. Most disconcerting was the way they seemed to float in the air around her. She passed Lula's bed and as she reached the bedroom door, it swung silently open before her.

Lula remembered the nun she had seen early that evening when she had registered. Why had she appeared in her room and why had the old porter lied? She threw on her robe determined to follow and force this strange visitor to speak to her. The nun moved gracefully down the hall and

Lula followed calling "Sister, wait and let me speak to you, please." But the gray-clad nun neither paused nor turned her head to acknowledge that she had heard. She reached the end of the hall and with a swirl of her garments, the nun turned suddenly around and looked Lula full in the face. She was astonishingly beautiful but the dark eyes were full of anguish. Her lips parted as if she were trying to tell Lula something and she seemed to be making a sign with her hands and gesturing toward her left.

At that moment Lula heard the sound of a door open down the hall behind her and voices. She turned at the interruption and when she looked back, the gray lady was gone. Bitterly disappointed she searched the stairwell at the end of the hall and even knocked on the doors of several nearby rooms. One door came open and she saw that at this end of the hall the rooms were not furnished or in use. The young teacher was close to panic but she managed to get back to her room where for the first time in her life Lula Tedder fainted.

When she awoke she could see the gray light of dawn at the edges of the drapes and it was the most glorious sight she had ever seen. The rain had stopped, the night had fled, the corners of the room were no longer dark—nor was there anywhere a shadowy form with misty gray robes floating around her! Lula dressed rapidly and stopped at the desk to pay her bill. The clerk ran his finger down the list of guests on the ledger.

"Jenkins, Thomas, Tedder——why, that's the name of a young man who married into the De Saurin family. This Inn used to be their home, you know."

"No, I didn't," said Lula who felt impatient but managed to smile politely. She paid for her room and the man made no further comment.

She had not driven many miles when the rain began again. Opaque sheets of water struck her windshield with such force she could barely see. Finally, she rolled down the steamy window to decide where she was and whether she was still on the right road. Ahead of her the road forked and she was about to bear right when suddenly the nun's gesture and frantic efforts to tell her something crossed her mind. Had she been pointing left? Lula thought she had and without being sure why or which was the route to take, she bore left.

By mid-afternoon she had reached her home in Asheville and the small Victorian house with its green shutters was a welcome sight. As she opened the front door and walked into the hall, her mother threw her arms around her.

"Lula, I've been so worried about you. Did you know that the bridge on the old road was out?"

"No, I didn't."

"Well, it has been out since the storm yesterday and if I could have phoned you, I would have but I didn't know where you would stay. I was so afraid that you would be in a hurry and try to take the short cut at the fork."

"The short cut at the fork where the roads branch off? You know, I had almost forgotten that spot where either road brings me out at the same place. The one on the left winds about a bit more, but for some reason I took it."

"Well, they would not have brought you out at the same place today," said her mother, and she was right.

There are old residents of Camden who say the ethereal gray lady walks on starless nights across the barriers of time to haunt the living. But always with compassion. And, if you should meet her you will know there is danger ahead. You will also know that you had a distant relative who once lived in France, a beautiful young nun named Eloise De Saurin.

The Ghost Ship

The doomed colonists saw it and so did the Indians

Alone figure stooped down at the water's edge silhouetted against the sky. It was a timeless scene that might easily have occurred a thousand or so years ago. In the late afternoon light the almost naked form of a man could be seen moving along the shoreline and gathering small shellfish. He was one of North Carolina's Hatteras Indians.

Straightening up suddenly the man gazed out to sea. Motionless and intent he watched the edge of the horizon where a small dark speck was visible. The speck grew larger and larger until the outline was the size of a toy boat, but gradually and unmistakably it became an impressive ship. Its sails stretched full and taut before the gusty autumn wind. With astonishment he saw the vessel head toward Roanoke Inlet.

He turned toward the woods cupping his hands around his mouth and then began beckoning urgently. Other Indians ran out on the beach to join him watching the big three-masted sailing ship go into the inlet. Some began to jump up and down, practically doubling up in their excitement and joy. Well aware of how shallow the inlet was, they knew the ship was certain to wreck. For hadn't many wrecked like this before? For over a hundred years vessels had been going to the bottom in inlets like this one along the Outer Banks and joyful Indians had been salvaging all sorts of unfamiliar but exciting riches including the nails that they prized so highly.

But this time the most astounding thing happened. With the wind behind it and the triangular flags atop each mast fluttering, this miraculous ship sailed right through the treacherous, shallow water with never a pause. Then it turned and proceeded safely on toward Roanoke Island. The Indians shielded their eyes against the rays of the setting sun to watch. It was an incredible sight and the bewildered savages waiting for the ship to run aground in the shallow water saw it become almost transparent as the afternoon sun shone through it until it faded away, disappearing before their very eyes!

Full of awe and fear they raced toward the undergrowth at the edge of the forest near the shore. A council meeting was held which lasted until the sun rose again. The wise men of the tribe offered many explanations concerning the appearance of the wondrous ship and what it meant.

Surprisingly close to the council meeting, dawn was breaking upon a group of men of a very different sort, led by a highly educated, keenly observant Englishman. It was 1703 and John Lawson* with a handful of companions was ex-

*Lawson's history of North Carolina has become a classic. Himself a gentleman and a scholar, his description of the state appeared first as part of John Steven's "A New Collection of Voyages and Travels; with Historical Accounts of Discoveries and Conquests in All Parts of the World." In 1709 Lawson's work appeared alone under the title of "A New Voyage to Carolina." The North Carolina legislature ordered the book reprinted in 1860 because the original printings had become exceedingly scarce.

ploring the northern portion of coastal North Carolina, that area which later was called the Outer Banks. Lawson and his men traveled by boat along the rivers and late one fall afternoon two Indians in a canoe paddled out to their boat. One threw beads in Lawson's boat as a sign of love and friendship. Since the explorers were tired he consented to the Indians' pleas to go ashore with them.

As soon as they landed they were joined by other Indians of the same tribe bringing a large store of fresh fish, mullet, shad and many other sorts, which they shared with the hungry travelers. Lawson and his men were much impressed by the friendliness and generosity of these tall, well-built Indians with their surprising gray eyes. No other Indians they had met possessed eyes of this color. Normally, their eyes were dark brown, sometimes verging on black.

After the bountiful meal was eaten under the large laurel and bay trees, it was plain the Indians were eager to tell the Englishmen something they considered of the utmost importance. The chief man among them, he who had thrown the beads into their boat, stepped forward and began speaking to Lawson. He gestured often toward the sea and spoke in such an excited manner that his story would have been difficult to follow if Lawson had not learned the language of a number of Indian tribes while roaming the coastal Carolinas.

As he waved a bronzed arm in the direction of the ocean the other tribesmen stood silently by occasionally nodding vehement assent. Lawson's comrades could catch the word for "by ship," "under full sail" and "talk in a book" which was the Indian way of describing a man who could read.

Lawson's eyes shone with excitement and his men could scarcely wait for the Indian to finish so that they might learn what he said. None of the Indians added to his story, it being their custom to listen respectfully to a speaker and not interrupt one another. When he had completed the story to his satisfaction, the Indian fell silent and looked at Lawson with unusual warmth and expectancy.

John Lawson responded with the word for brother at the same time gesturing in a friendly fashion to assure the Indian of his feeling of kinship.

Now it was the Englishmen's turn to hear the story.

"This is not the first time I have heard of this man's experience," said Lawson. "It has been told me by many an Indian wise man when I have been in these parts of Carolina. This man says that many times their tribesmen have seen a ship they were certain was an English sailing vessel come over the horizon and sail quite close to land. It has happened during the day as well as on moonlit nights. Someone among them would look out to sea and there would be an imposing ship under full sail. Quite often it would sail along for a considerable time so that others would gather and watch the ship in amazement as it glided through the water.

"But each time they attempted to paddle out to it in their canoes, it would disappear, filling them with fear and awe. He believes this ship is the one which brought the first colonists to this Island and the Indians call it Sir Walter Raleigh's ship." Lawson stopped to admonish some of the men who were smiling.

"The truth of this has been affirmed to me by men of the best credit in the country." These men say that "several of their ancestors were white people and could talk in a book (read as white men did), the truth of which is confirmed by gray eyes being found frequently amongst these Indians and no others."

Lawson went on to recall to his men the story of the ill-fated colony which John White left in the summer of 1587 in order to bring back badly needed supplies from England. Unfortunately, upon his arrival in England in November, he found his country at war with Spain. Every ship was being commandeered for the struggle and although he begged to be allowed to return to the colony with the supplies they desperately needed, he was refused permission.

Meanwhile the colonists suffered and waited watching day and night for the ship's return. In the spring, White optimistically fitted out a small fleet to leave for Roanoke Island. But the Queen

of England seized the ships before they could sail. Winning the war with Spain came first.

Those of the colonists who had been able to survive the winter were probably still hopeful. One can imagine them watching the horizon anxiously day after day expecting the arrival of the vessel which would bring the long-awaited clothes, food, medicine and ammunition to relieve their suffering. What rejoicing there would be. As they huddled cold and half-starved along the windswept shores of the island, perhaps they began to have hallucinations. Is it possible their eyes began to supply the ship they wanted so badly to see sailing along that vast, empty, gray-blue horizon of the 1500's?

Some died from sickness, others hunger and, no doubt, they felt more and more abandoned and alone. Their Indian companions who had helped them survive the winter, probably began to watch with them scanning the horizon for the ship the white men talked of constantly, lived for and were so certain would come.

Tragically enough, and despite all his determination, for after all, he had left his daughter and grandaughter on the island, it was not until August of 1590 that John White was able to return. He set sail on the Hopewell, one of three ships sent to raid Spanish vessels off the coast of Cuba and capture whatever cargo or treasure they could. Then they were to sail northward up the coast and aid the colonists.

At daybreak on August 18, 1590 White and several sailors got into a small boat and paddled through rough seas to shore. They walked through the woods and rounded North West Point to the place he had left the colonists three years before. White stumbled in his excitement as he climbed the dunes of sand.

At the top of a forested dune White found a tree on which without any Maltese cross as a sign of distress, had been carved the letters 'CRO.' Bewildered, he walked down to where the settlement had been. There was the high wooden palisade around an enclosure. But the little houses inside were gone. Every building had been taken down. Scattered here and there were some iron bars and pigs of lead, some shot and four cannon. On a post at the right-hand side of the entrance he discovered the word 'CROATOAN.' White thought that this probably meant they had gone inland with Manteo and his friends to Croatoan Island and filled with excitement he wanted to go on southward to the island to look for them.

By now a storm was blowing up. The seas were so rough the men were unable even to load fresh water, the Hopewell nearly ran aground and the anchor rope broke so that she had lost one of her two anchors. The weather was becoming more and more treacherous so that with water and food short and only one anchor left they decided it was too dangerous to continue the search.

Completing his story about the ghost ship the Indians told of seeing and the return of White to look for the colonists, John Lawson stared thoughtfully out to sea. It was over one hundred years ago since Captain White had left the doomed colonists on Roanoke Island. Was there really such a thing as a ghost ship? And, if it did exist was it as one Indian wise man had said "an omen" to all the Indians living along the coast that they were in danger from the white man, and that the appearance of the phantom vessel was a forewarning? No one knows.

Reports which are sometimes still heard of a phantom ship sailing over the water through inlets where no real ship could ever go remain as much a mystery today as the fate of the colonists themselves.

120

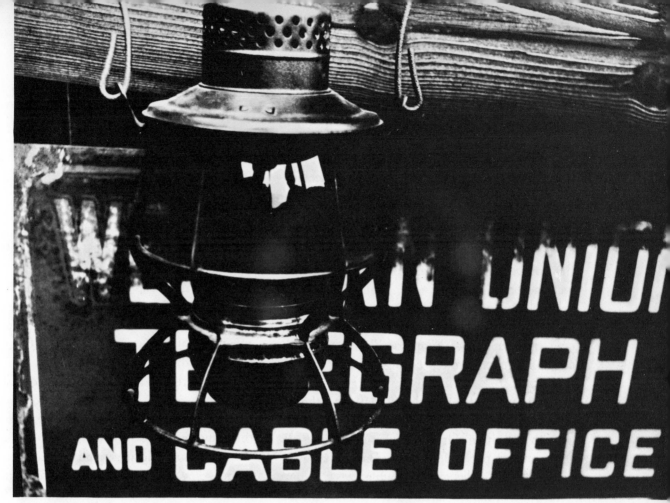

The railroad telegraph sent word the freight train had been robbed.

Railroad BILL

For many years this Alabama bandit eluded the law
and some still see his ghost near the railroad tracks.

THE BLACK ROBINHOOD

"Railroad Bill mighty bad man,
Shoot dem lights out de brakeman's han'."

There were no screens at the windows of the little unpainted ramshackly house near the railroad tracks. But the old lady was used to that. When the sun went down and the night's chill began to settle in she went to each window and hooked the wooden shutter. The old lady fastened them not only to keep out the cold night air but to keep out whatever else might be lurking in the darkness whether man, beast or spirit.

She banked the fire so she would have hot coals in the morning, although she didn't need them to start up the wood in the old wood stove for she had nothing to heat on it, no food and no money to buy food with. Since she had become too old and too crippled by arthritis to work, she had gotten a small check from the welfare but toward the last of the month there never seemed to be enough left even for food. This morning she had fried and eaten a small piece of fatback, all that was left.

She was glad to crawl under the worn quilt on the iron bed and go to sleep for that was the best way not to think about being hungry. Before long, however, she heard a shot ring out and it came from close by. A train's whistle began to emit desperate "toot, toot, toots" and then she could hear men's voices calling out and lots of shouting.

"Don't never hunt trouble," she lay there thinking and not moving. "Bad enuf to be hongry, don' have to go runnin' out to see what everythin's all about and git put in de jail, too. Dat's what happens when po' folks gits in trouble."

About that time Aunt Elly felt the house shake. It sounded like somebody had come running and taken one big jump, landing right on her back porch. She plumb forgot the misery in her bones and was out of bed and at the back door before you could say spit. Next came a rattling and a clatter on the floor of her porch. She opened the door just in time to see a tall black man standing out there with a big grin stretched across his face, and then he was gone, a straight, broad shouldered figure running across her yard and into the pine woods.

Scattered all over her porch were cans of food and vegetables.

"God bless Railroad Bill," she said looking toward the woods and then as fast as she could she gathered every can and had them in the house and under her bed. This done Aunt Elly crawled back under the quilt. She did not have long to wait.

Soon there was a bounding on her cabin door, It shook the shack from the roof to the floor. Aunt Elly got up and opened the door. There stood the sheriff and a few men more. He asked Aunt Elly if she'd seen Railroad Bill, that he'd robbed a train and would shoot to kill. The old lady made like she was scared to death, said "Oh, mistuh sheriff, keep dat man way from heah. He mighty bad fellah an I hope he don' come neah."

The sheriff said, "Don't you worry, Aunt Elly. We'll get him this time shore. We brung along some bloodhounds. He won't bother folks no more." He turned around and stepped down from the porch saying, "Tell me, boys, did we bring three hounds or four? Seemed to me we took just three and now I see one more."

But no one paid it any mind and through the woods they went. The dogs were snufflin' on the ground like they had got the scent. But they came right out on the other side with no Railroad Bill in sight, and the sheriff saw the fourth hound dog had vanished in the night. The hair rose on the sheriff's neck and he turned to a friend and said, "That was no bloodhound that ran with the pack, that was Railroad Bill, instead. He's led us a merry chase tonight and he's laughin' in his bed."

For many years this Alabama bandit eluded the law. A black Robinhood, Railroad Bill robbed freight trains along the Louisville and Nashville Railroad, distributing his loot among the poor. Some say the police finally caught him. Others say his ghost still haunts the pine woods near the tracks, and when some poor old lady finds food outside her door she is more than apt to look each way for the law and then whisper under her breath "God bless Railroad Bill!"

Near this lonely depot in Alabama, Railroad Bill's ghost has been seen walking along the tracks.

The *Haunted* Car

They did not even want to ride in this car for something very strange had happened in it.

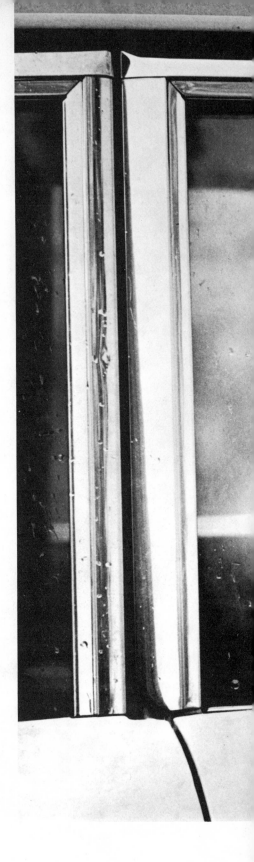

Most people are happy to own a new car, but recently a minister and his wife who live in Mississippi wished they did not have one. They wanted very badly to get rid of it. In fact they would even have been glad to have their old car back. It was not that this car did not run perfectly, for it did. But they did not even want to ride in it for something very strange happened when they were in this car and Bill Jamison and his wife were afraid.

It was a brand new shiny gold color four door sedan, a gift from the church Reverend Jamison had served for the past three years. After his secondhand automobile which had the temperament of a donkey about starting, along with a host of other equally endearing qualities, left him

stranded half-way to a wedding he was to perform one Saturday, his congregation's natural generosity got the better of them and they decided to give Mr. Jamison a new car.

His wife, Charlene, could sit in it without the springs jabbing her, the children could roll down the windows without the young minister having to get out and guide the glass back up with his hand if it rained, and the Jamisons began to feel for the first time that having a car was not a series of problems. All went well for the first two weeks.

It was on a Sunday night that Bill and Charlene Jamison decided they would drive to Memphis to see some friends. They were late getting off since Bill had attended a meeting at the church first and both were tired. The Jamisons were driving along from Tupelo to Memphis when suddenly a woman's voice spoke up from the back seat.

"I hope you don't mind my riding with you?" she said, and the minister and his wife turned around to find a little old lady leaning forward with an anxious expression on her face.

Deciding that she must have gotten into the car when they had stopped for gas before leaving Tupelo, Mrs. Jamison assured her they were glad to have her.

"Where can we take you?" asked Jamison.

"You are both very kind," replied the old lady. "I have been sick for several weeks and I'm trying to get to the home of my daughter who lives in Memphis."

"Why, that's no trouble for us at all," said Charlene Jamison. "That's where we happen to be going tonight. You just tell us where we can drop you off."

The little old lady seemed pathetically appreciative and gave them the street address of her daughter's home in Memphis. After that their passenger did not seem particularly inclined to

talk and finding herself more tired than she realized, Charlene Jamison fell asleep.

Her husband was intent on his own thoughts and the road so he did not try to make conversation. They drove for some time in silence and it was not until he stopped at a light on the outskirts of Memphis that Charlene awoke. Feeling they had ignored the old lady, she turned around to speak to her. But, to her amazement, the back seat was empty!

Could she have fallen out of the car without their knowing it? The young couple were shocked and frightened. Something dreadful must have happened to their passenger. They could not imagine how she had left the car without their knowing it. Bill Jamison turned around and drove a number of miles along the road, slowing at country crossroads where he had stopped or paused for caution lights, and the pair strained their eyes looking through the darkness expecting to see the body of the old lady lying beside the road. But they saw no sign of her.

Becoming discouraged, they decided the only thing to do was to turn back to Memphis and find the home of the old lady's daughter. They located the street and the house number she had given them and rang the bell. An attractive young housewife in her early thirties opened the door.

The Jamisons began to tell about finding her mother on the back seat of the car and their distress over her disappearance. As they told her about the old lady's asking them to bring her to this address, tears came to the young woman's eyes.

"My mother has been dead for six months," she said. "This is the third time this has happened and she has appeared to one couple several times."

It was just a few weeks later that the Jamisons decided to visit an auto dealer in Jackson, Mississippi. The salesman was puzzled.

"Now, which car is it out there you said was yours?"

"The gold colored sedan."

"And that's the one you want to trade for another car?"

"Yes," replied the minister patiently.

"Sorry, sir, I wasn't trying to be rude. But it's not often somebody brings a car in that looks like new and says they want to trade it. Been having any motor trouble?"

"No, the motor's in good condition. I just want to trade cars. There's a car over there," and he pointed to a brand new gold colored sedan.

"Yes, sir, but that's the same model you're driving."

"I know that. Do you mind telling me how much I can trade for?"

The young salesman went out and looked at the mileage on the minister's car. Then he did some figuring in his office.

"I'm sorry, but it's going to come to $750.00. You know your car does have some mileage on it and we can't sell it for new."

"I understand that. Can we finance the difference?"

The salesman figured out what the monthly payments would be and the minister and his wife signed the necessary papers.

After they were through he said, "If you don't mind, sir, I sure would like to know why you wanted to trade that car."

"Mind? No, not a bit. That car is haunted and I don't ever want to see it again!"

With that Bill and Charlene Jamison drove off in the car they had just purchased leaving the salesman staring after them, if anything more bewildered than ever. He gazed over at the car they had left behind them. Was that his imagination or had someone gotten into the car? It looked almost like the profile of a little old lady sitting on the back seat. He shook his head in disbelief and walked a little closer, but when he could see in the rear side window better, there was no one there at all.

He glanced around to be sure none of the other salesmen had seen his odd behaviour. Better sell that car before we're all crazy around here, he thought, and he walked toward a couple who had just come into the salesroom.

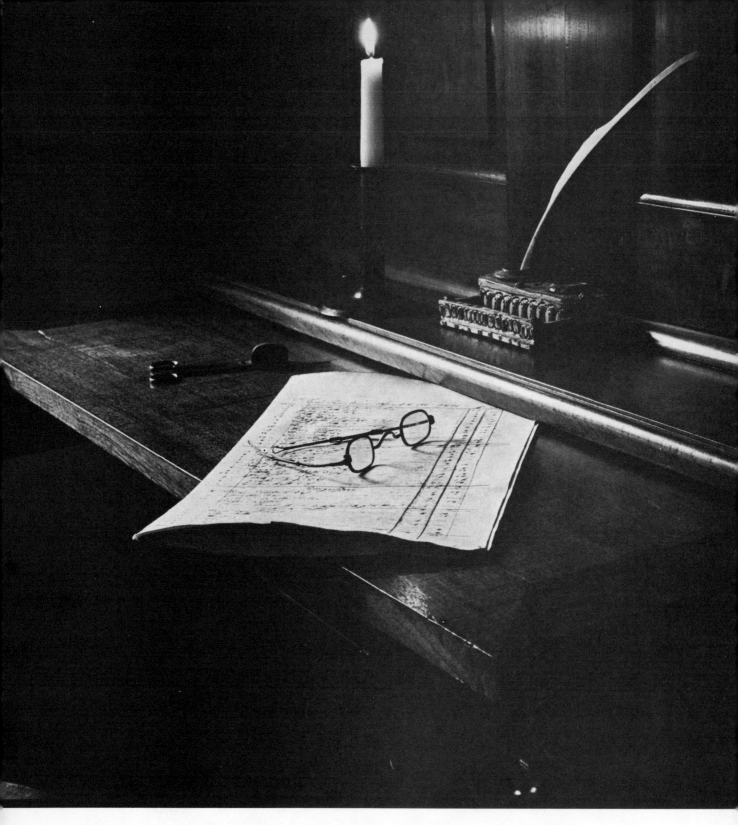

The tavern keeper's desk looks the same today as it did a hundred years ago. The Tavern is part of the Old Salem restoration at Winston-Salem.

The Talking Corpse

The keeper of Old Salem Tavern never forgot the night a dead man brought him a message

As the keeper of Salem Tavern busily greeted new arrivals, he had not the slightest premonition that this night was to be the start of a most unusual chain of events.

It was a bitterly cold November evening and a drizzling rain added to the discomfort of travelers. Many decided to stop early and enjoy the Tavern's cheer. It was a house of entertainment with a widespread reputation for hospitality and had often been host to distinguished visitors. George Washington himself lodged here for two days on his 1791 visit to North Carolina.

As the hour grew late the social rooms emptied, the guests retired, and the tavern keeper sat alone before his upright walnut desk. His office door opened off one side of the rear of the large tavern hall. Behind it was the sitting room used by his own family. At the left of his desk was a small window which admitted enough light to allow him to see his accounts. And at the far end of the tiny cubicle stood a tall wardrobe.

Oftentimes before he went to bed the tavern keeper would check his menu for the following day. As his eyes scanned the listing of mutton, venison, vegetables, kraut, cheese, and gingerbread, he thought he heard a faint rapping sound. He stepped out into the hall and listened. There was someone at the front door.

While he threw back the heavy bolt the hall clock chimed half after eleven. He opened the door and a man staggered across the threshold. A wave of irritation swept over the tavern keeper at the thought of having to deal with a drunken traveler at this hour—and then he saw his guest's face. It was gray and drawn with suffering.

This was no drunk. It was a desperately ill man.

The tavern keeper summoned the hostler to care for his visitor's mare, seated the man in a chair in the gentlemen's room and went to arouse his two slaves. One he sent after a doctor "with all possible haste," and the other he directed to help the sick man to his room.

The man was in such anguish that he could not even tell the tavern keeper his name. So the keeper decided to wait until morning to register him. By now the doctor had arrived. He examined the patient, administered some medicine from his bag and then drew the tavern keeper to one side.

"This man is gravely ill. If he is not much improved by morning, you must call me."

Shortly afterwards the patient lapsed into a coma and before morning he was dead.

Unfortunately his clothes were not marked nor did the contents of his saddlebags reveal a single clue to his identity.

After a decent burial ceremony the Parish

Graveyard received his remains and the saddle-bags were placed in the office wardrobe on the bare chance that they might some day be claimed.

Several days later the innkeeper's servants began to mutter uneasily. The slaves and the hostler talked of strange goings-on in the shadowy corridors of the tavern. They were reluctant to go through the basement alone. The hostler was as jumpy as the young maid. Nervously they claimed that "something" was haunting the place.

The tavern keeper at first laughed; then he grew increasingly exasperated as he tried without success to allay the fears of his staff. Nothing he could say seemed to calm them or discourage the apprehensive glances they cast over their shoulders as they went about their work. One night one of the slaves dropped a heavy tray which he was taking to the dining room. Afterwards he swore something had followed him into the hall.

Finally, one night, while the tavern keeper was in his office struggling over his accounts, a young maid burst in upon him, pale with fright.

"Something awful is out in that hall!" she declared hysterically.

Overcome by annoyance, the tavern keeper left the maid trembling in his office and strode out into the corridor. At first it appeared to be empty. Then to his utter amazement he heard a scraping sound and a shadowy, faceless form appeared before him.

He managed to conquer his impulse to flee and heard a voice speak to him. In hollow tones the voice begged him to notify "my brother of my death." It gave the dead traveler's name and the name of a brother in Texas. Then the hall was again empty.

When he returned to his desk the tavern keeper's hands were shaking but he grasped his pen the more firmly and began a letter to the address in Texas which the voice had given him. He described his guest and went into detail about his illness and death.

It was not long before he received an answer. The reply confirmed his guest's identity and asked that the saddlebags be forwarded to the Texas home.

The instructions of the spirit were no sooner carried out than the peculiar manifestations ceased, nor did the servants ever complain again about the tavern being haunted.

The ghost had departed as soon as his errand was accomplished. But for the rest of his life the keeper of Salem Tavern told this story of "the talking corpse" and steadfastly vouched for its truth.

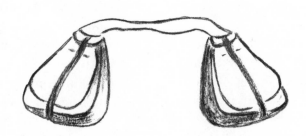

The hall of the old Salem tavern

The Hound of Goshen

**The shadows of the old stagecoach road were frightening,
indeed, for travelers pursued by the ghostly white dog**

The ghost that pursues travelers as they pass over the old Buncombe Road through Goshen has staked out a five-mile stretch of the road as his own.

He has struck terror into the heart of many a traveler between Ebenezer Church in Maybinton township, Newberry County, and Goshen Hill in South Carolina's Union County. After dark is his time to roam and he has never been known to stray from his accustomed path.

It was in 1855 that Dr. George Douglass lived in a white-columned mansion on a high bluff overlooking the stagecoach route from Charleston to Asheville. The road below the bluff was narrow, its banks on either side of the deep cut high and thickly forested. The sun seldom penetrated the road's dense shade. Often travel along it was slow because of mud or fallen limbs and to proceed with any speed it was necessary to go by horse.

On a late October night a slave of William Hardy in Maybinton got sick. Hardy sent a young slave boy by mule to fetch Dr. Douglass from Goshen Hill four miles away, saying, "Ride fast but don't overheat him."

Dr. and Mrs. Douglass were awakened by a series of terrified screams. The trembling boy fell in their door, crying, "Keep dat varmint from gittin' me."

Dr. Douglass closed the hall door and lit the lamp. The boy was almost incoherent with fear.

"Marse Doc, I is so scart dat I would hab died if'n I hadn't got to yo' doah when I did. Marse Billy sarnt me here tuh fetch you to see Sam, 'cause he is awful ailin'."

"Is Sam dying?" asked the doctor.

"No suh, Sam ain't dyin'. Leas' he wa'nt when I lef'."

"Well, why are you so scared?" questioned Douglass.

"Marse Billy 'low when I lef', ride fas' but don't you let my mule git broke out in no big sweat. I wuz ridin' along jus' as moderate as I could 'til I got to de white folks' Ebenezer Church.

"Hit was there I heered somethin' and, Marse, I looked back of me and seed de awfullest varmint I eber seed in my life, an' Lawd! I hope I ain't gwine neber see such a thing agin' as long as I lib."

"What foolish thing did you see?" inquired the doctor in some exasperation.

"Marse, it wusn't nothin' foolish. When I heered dat noise, I looked around and I seed de terrublist, whitest, biggest dog I is eber heered of in my life. I stuck my heels in dat ole mule and he bruk out in de fastes' run. I thought we wuz leavin' dat dog when all at onct it got in front of de mule. Dat mule reared up and I jus' did miss fallin' offen him. When I looked agin hit was stretchin' hit's eyes at me. All de time me an' dat mule was jus' shakin' an' runnin'!"

"Where do you think the dog came from?" asked the doctor.

"Hit muster come out of de ole Evans grave-yard down by de chu'ch, Marster."

"How far did it follow you?"

"Dat thing neber lef' us til I started hollerin' an' driv inter yo' lane."

"You say that your master wants me to come and see Sam?"

"Yes, suh, Marse George."

"You go back home and tell your master that I will be there at daylight."

The Negro boy fell to the floor in a frenzy of fear. "Lord God, Marse George!" he pleaded. "I can't go down dat road no mo' til day!"

Dr. Douglass went out into the yard to look at the mule. He saw that the animal was wringing wet with sweat and still trembling. The doctor called one of his own servants and had him take the mule to the barn and then take the distraught young Negro in for the night.

Early next day Dr. Douglass and the slave rode

to the Hardy plantation. Along the way the boy excitedly pointed out different spots where "dat dog come out las' night."

Many times since then this strange apparition has been seen in Goshen. It still causes much alarm and a number of respected and wholly reliable witnesses have seen it.

Dr. Jim Coefield saw it and was never able to account for it. He had an affectionate dog which often followed him but after they encountered the "ghost dog" his own would leave the road at a certain spot and go through the woods until the doctor had passed the trail of the ghost. Then he would rejoin his master and trot along beside him.

Berry Sanders, a Negro boy of about seventeen, saw the ghost dog one night in April of 1936. Berry worked for a Mr. Watt Henderson and every Saturday night he had to go through Goshen on his way home. On the night of April 18 when he was going through the side gate at "The Oaks" he heard a noise. Glancing back he saw the vicious looking apparition trotting after him. It was the "Hound of Goshen."

Berry's home was a mile distant and he ran every foot of the way. The neighbors heard his screams. When the boy reached the safety of his home, the dog turned back and vanished into the woods.

There are many varying accounts. The ghost dog may leap through a closed iron gate and disappear or it may spring out from a thicket along the old road. Horses and mules along this road often behave as if they are badly frightened, much to the bewilderment of their drivers. For it is not unusual for animals with their acute senses to be first aware of the hound's peculiar presence.

And if you should decide on a pleasant evening to take a horseback ride along the old road, and your steed rears back violently, or the hair along your dog's back rises, you will do well to beware the "Hound of Goshen."

For he is there.

The Ring

Death brings a coveted ring – and disaster – to a greedy young woman

Mary was the proud, petulant one of the two sisters, while Kate was gentle hearted and kind. Orphaned during their teens the girls lived in a small cottage from which could be heard the roar of the surf when the wind was high.

The men of Dare County along the Outer Banks of North Carolina first begin to test their mettle against the honing of the sea while they are still boys. And young David Blount was one of the bravest of this "bred to the sea" breed. No night was too wild or treacherous waters too turbulent for his rescue boat when the call came to bring in terrified passengers from a wrecked ship.

David courted Kate with the same fierceness of purpose that made him thrust his eager young face into the driving rain over the stormy Atlantic. At first Mary tried to divert his attentions from her meek younger sister to herself. And when that failed she took an intense dislike to him. David knew it and cared not a whit.

After a short time Kate agreed to marry him and David produced a diamond ring of surpassing beauty which he placed upon her finger. When the winds battered the little cottage at night and the sound of the sea rose in a crashing crescendo, Kate would look at the flashing ring and say, "The fire from this ring somehow warms

my spirit and I know he'll come home to me again."

But one night the sea was the victor. Savage waves assaulted the cape and the tiny, storm-tossed boat which David rode like a young Viking was struck a shattering blow. The mountainous waves crushed it as if it were a child's toy.

When they came to tell her, Kate said nothing. From then on she went silently about her tasks at home and in the village. She rarely spoke, never smiled, until as a neighbor woman said, "The girl is like a flower which the frost has touched."

As Kate became more and more remote Mary's vivaciousness seemed to increase. There was an almost expectant air about her. Occasionally someone would see Kate looking at her ring and only then did she resemble her former self for her face would take on a strange glow.

One morning the wife of a fisherman who lived nearby heard a pounding at her door and Mary's voice crying out, "Help me! Help me! Kate is dead."

That night Mary refused to let anyone keep her company as she sat with the body. Her grief seemed too great to share. A small candle burned near the head of the coffin and Mary sat at its side. For several hours she barely moved. Then she leaned forward and looked over the side of the wooden box. Her body swayed backward slightly as if hesitating, then leaned forward poised over the casket. This time her hand crept over the edge. She grasped something, tugged, gasped slightly then tugged again, every muscle tensed.

Successful, she sank back into her chair with a sigh of deep satisfaction. A moment later she rose and held her hand up to the light of the candle. On her finger glowed the diamond.

At the funeral the sobs of Kate's sister were pathetic to hear, and as she raised her hands dramatically and wrung them in her sorrow the magnificent diamond showed off to advantage.

Several nights later Mary sat alone in the cottage. The night was a wicked one and wind and sea played an eerie duet. Then came a calling at the door above the sound of the weather, "Mary, I'm so cold. Oh, Mary, please let me come in." This happened night after night until Mary could stand it no longer. Finally, she sought the advice of a neighbor woman who suggested

she ask her visitor to come in and warm herself.

That night when she heard the same pleading voice at the door, she called out to it to come in. The wind blew the door open with a clatter and a shadowy form drifted through it coming to rest quite close to where Mary stood.

"Why, Kate," said Mary. "Where are your beautiful white hands?"

"In the grave, so-o cold. Oh, Mary, what have you done to me to leave me so cold in the grave?"

"Well, Kate, where is your beautiful diamond ring?"

With that the specter seized Mary's hand.

It was mid-morning when the fisherman's wife could conceal her curiosity no longer. She came over to find out how her advice had fared.

She knocked, then she called but there was no answer. Opening the unbarred door she found Mary sitting in front of the dead embers of the fire. She answered not one of the woman's stream of questions. She simply sat looking at her left hand. The fourth finger was badly bruised; the diamond ring was gone. Nor was she ever seen wearing it again.

The Phantom Rider
of Bush River

Her lover kept his promise to return, though not the way she had longed that he would

The earliest account of the Phantom Rider of Bush River appears in a copy of *The Rising Sun* dated April 25, 1860. Published just a year before the War Between the States, it is one of the few Carolina ghost stories to have been in written form for more than a century.

In a modest log house near Bobo's Mills on the Bush River lived a Quaker father with his lovely young daughter named Charity and a stalwart son. Although South Carolina was going through the turbulence of the Revolutionary War, the life which Charity and her family shared was a quiet one.

Its tranquillity was rippled only by the occasional, carefully concealed visits of brave young Henry Galbreath. He lost no opportunity to visit Charity when scouting trips for his country brought him nearby. He came at the risk of his life for there were many Tories about who would have given much to catch him.

One dark summer night when flecks of clouds swam over the face of the moon, young Galbreath came to visit Charity. He had come to tell her "good-by" for he had enlisted in the Continental Army.

"But one year from this day, my dear, I shall be back whether dead or alive. My horse and I will come galloping up the river road, so wait for me, my lovely lass." And Charity promised. It was July of 1780 when young Henry Galbreath left to join the American Army with which General Horatio Gates was marching south to defeat Cornwallis. Unfortunately for Henry, the Continental Commander was to be defeated at Camden and both the Carolinas plunged into a night of darkness for the American cause in the South.

After the defeat at Camden, it is not clear whether young Henry, for a time, joined the small band of guerrilla fighters led by the "Swamp Fox" Francis Marion. Marion's men represented about the only organized resistance left in South Carolina for the moment against the British. General Nathanael Greene, who had been sent south by Washington to rebuild the American Army at Charlotte was reassembling his forces.

In January of 1781 the tide of the battle began to turn. Henry, who was familiar with the frontier Piedmont, became a scout for William

Washington's cavalry. His knowledge of the red clay country of the Catawba and the French Broad River Valley became invaluable. As both the British and the American armies moved across the Carolinas a tall, blue robed rider moved with them. Galbreath not only knew the country, but he had come to know the enemy and wherever he went his reputation for courage accompanied him.

When the major engagement with the British came at Cowpens, it was on ground which General Morgan had carefully selected because of the advantage it gave to the Americans. The Cowpens area was a fairly open pasture where for many years traders had assembled cattle on their way to market. Thus, the rather unglamorous name for what was to become one of the great American victories of the war. Henry had ridden through this area many times down the Old Mill Gap Road and north to the ford at Broad River.

Morgan's men formed their line of battle according to plan. First the sharpshooters, then the militia and behind the militia the main line of Continentals and Virginians. William Washington's cavalry was to rally and protect the militia if the necessity arose. While the ragged Continentals waited, the British line emerged from the forest at the far end of the meadow. There were foot-soldiers in scarlet and white, kilted Highlanders and horsemen in bright hues of green and scarlet with plumed brass helmets.

The battle was a fierce one but before the hour had passed the British began to fall back.

A bitterly disappointed Tarleton accompanied by several of his officers prepared to flee. As they left the field of the disaster, one of the officers turned and fired a shot at a pursuing member of Washington's cavalry. The shot lodged in the heart of Henry Galbreath.

At the little frontier cabin on the Bush River, Charity still waited unaware of her sweetheart's death. In cheerful repetition of household chores, sewing in the afternoon under the trees and loving preparation of meals for her father and brother, the year passed.

On the day appointed for Henry's return, Charity walked often to the door of the little cabin.

Shielding her eyes from the sun, she gazed hopefully down the river road. In the afternoon, she sat beside the river and tried to lose herself in watching it shimmer past in the sunlight.

But within she was waiting . . . waiting for the galloping sound of a horse's hoofs, and for the first time in her life the familiar, silently flowing river seemed an alien presence.

That night she let her hair down about her neck and went to bed—but not to sleep. About two o'clock she heard a peculiar sound as if the wind were rising and in the distance a rhythmic galloping which grew louder until she heard it stop outside the house.

When Charity opened the door, there was a flash of light. She saw a rider astride a handsome steed. Proudly he sat his mount and from his shoulders there flowed a blue-black robe. The flash of light came twice again. Then off sped horse and rider disappearing down the river road.

The next day Charity and her father looked all about the house and road. There were no tracks on the ground nor traces to show that any living thing had been there. She knew then that Henry had returned as he had promised—but not alive.

Henry Galbreath had joined his country's forces during a period of defeat. A year later in July, when he appeared as a ghost, the battles of Guilford Courthouse and Holbrooks Hill had already been fought and the American cause saved in the Carolinas. After Galbreath's death, the British were never quite able to win another victory in the South. Cornwallis retreated into Virginia where he surrendered in October.

In later years on moonless nights, the sound of hoofbeats was often heard beginning at the battlefield of Cowpens and continuing up the road toward the little log house on the Bush River.

Galbreath's ghost or the Phantom Rider as it is most often called, became a harbinger of defeat for the British as they never again won a significant battle in the South.

he Witch Cat

Tim Farrow met a frightful death because he failed to recognize a witch in the form of a beautiful woman

In the stormy and uncertain days just before the Revolutionary War a miller and his small daughter lived near Edenton, North Carolina. To Tim Farrow the British occupation of Boston and talk of the king's oppression seemed remote, indeed, from daily tasks.

His Brownrigg Mill sat beside a long earthen dam with tall cypress trees on either side. The pond was one of the largest in that vicinity. There had always been talk—to which Tim paid little heed—that its dark amber waters were bottomless.

The day's work done, the miller would fish for a while along the bank and meditate as the last rays of the sun sifted through the cypress trees. One evening at dusk he saw a figure in a small boat approaching him from the far edge of the pond. He had never ventured to the opposite bank for the dark woods which fringed it contained for him elements of mystery and dread.

At first the shadows on the water were so deep that he could not tell whether the figure in the boat was a man or woman. But much to his astonishment when the boat reached him a woman raised her arm and pushed back her bonnet to reveal the loveliest face he had ever seen.

"My journey to these parts has been a long one. And on the way my husband died," said the young woman. "Can you tell me if there is a place close by where I might lodge for the night?"

Tim Farrow's heart went out to her. It had not been long since the death of his own wife, and this lovely creature seemed so pathetically alone and helpless.

"My small daughter and I live in yonder cottage by the mill," replied Tim. "You are welcome to share what little we have."

The young woman smiled at him gratefully and he marveled at the redness of the lips curving over her small white teeth. She gathered her full black cape around her with one hand and placed the other in his as he helped her from her boat.

That night for the first time in months Tim Farrow sat down to a delicious supper and the delights of feminine companionship. Faye, as his guest called herself, was not only a fine cook but utterly beguiling. Her hair had the sheen of black satin and while he talked her large amber colored eyes fixed themselves upon him in a manner which made him feel that surely he was a most entertaining fellow. The crude, good natured miller had never met such a woman before. Why, he felt as if he could grind corn all day and come home lighthearted as a king.

Faye stayed on, with one day following another in this happy fashion. And when the first traveling minister passed their way the two were married. The miller's only care now was the aversion which his small daughter showed for the newcomer. Occasionally Faye would try to touch the child only to have her cringe and draw away. Then sparks of yellow fire would glint in the wife's beautiful eyes.

Tim began to think that his neighbors were jealous of his good fortune. It had seemed to start while he was away on a hunting trip. Faye had spent the night with a neighbor. And afterwards the woman told that she had found her big feather bed with only a little round spot mashed down in the middle just as if a cat had slept there. After that some began to make no secret of the fact that they believed Tim's wife to be a witch.

Troubles piled up for Tim. Along with the gossip, his business at the mill began to dwindle. At the same time he sensed that his young wife was tiring of him. Often he would come home in the afternoon from the mill to find her curled up asleep in her bed. He would fix their supper and generally after the meal she became more animated and vivacious.

Unfortunately, the slacking off of Tim's business was accompanied by a series of mishaps to the mill itself. He would begin to grind the grain only to find the grinding wheels jerking, jumping and sending off blue sparks. Then he would discover that nails had been placed in the grain hoppers. Sometimes when he opened the mill door in the morning Tim found sacks of corn slashed open and grain scattered all over the floor.

The angry miller could only believe that his neighbors were tormenting him. And he decided to catch whoever was playing these cruel tricks. One night instead of walking over to the country store as was sometimes his habit, he left the path to the store and went back to his mill. Letting himself in quietly, Tim hid behind the grain bags to wait for the mischief makers.

He had not been crouched there long before he heard the wind rise outside and the rumble of thunder. Soon a heavy downpour of rain beat upon the wood shingled roof and wind whistled through the crevices of the old mill. In the shattering crashes of thunder the mill quaked as if all the wheels were grinding and trembling at once. The brawny miller was not easily frightened, but the storm was so violent that he began to feel uneasy.

In a little while it spent itself but as it did a deafening din of frog voices rose from the pond. And he could not help remembering that the hoarse voiced creatures were said to be in league with the devil. When an owl screeched eerily from somewhere in the swamp's depths Tim Farrow could feel his flesh tingle with real fear. A sense of dread engulfed him.

At that moment there came a sharp, staccato pounding on the door—as if a dozen broomsticks were rapping against it. Tim sprang from behind the sacks and seized an ax which he had placed beside him in the event of trouble. There was a brief moment of silence. Then the door of the mill flew open. In rushed a horde of tremendous cats. Backs humped and teeth bared, the cats began to inscribe menacing circles around him. As they passed they struck viciously at him with their outstretched paws.

The terrified miller soon saw that if he did not defend himself he would be clawed to death. Grasping his ax with both hands he swung mightily at a ferocious cat springing straight at him. The face with its flashing yellow eyes was close upon him as his ax swept through the air and landed on the animal's right paw, completely severing it. The cat gave one terrible cry of pain

and with ear-piercing screams and caterwauling the whole band fled out the door through which they had come.

Bleeding from the scratches the cats had inflicted, Tim stumbled out of the mill and back to his cottage. He found his wife in their bedroom. She lay on the bed in a rapidly widening pool of blood. To his horror he saw that it flowed from her right arm.

The arm had been neatly severed at the wrist.

Before the wretched man could speak his wife leaped out of the bed and her body took on the shape of a monstrous cat. Eyes blazing, it streaked past him out of the house.

As he stood like a man in a nightmare, struggling to recover himself, he heard the menacing sound of rushing water. He knew he must get to the dam gate before the roaring freshet reached it. Tim Farrow ran with frantic speed along the dam to raise the gate and save the mill. But he was too late. As he ran the dam began to tremble beneath him. The trees at the edge tottered crazily. Then the earth gave way.

With a terrified scream the miller lost his footing and toppled into the rushing black flood. As he went under his arms thrashed the water and his hands sought desperately for something to cling to.

In a few seconds more than a hundred feet of the mill dam had been swept away. Some said the bottomless depths of the pond claimed Tim Farrow's body forever. But another tale was told when the lights were low and the children safely asleep.

'Twas said then that a lone fisherman found the body floating near the darkly forested shore opposite the dam . . . And one tightly clenched hand held fast to the cleanly severed paw of a cat!

The Gray Man

His appearance means danger is near, and those who see him do well to heed his warning

He has strolled the strand at Pawley's Island since 1822. And when the Gray Man walks, danger is close at hand. For it has long been the practice of this benign apparition to show himself as a warning of impending disaster. His presence was again reported just before the Tidal Wave of 1893 near the old house now owned by the F. W. Lachicottes. And he is most likely to show himself in late September or October during the hurricane season.

The legend of the Gray Man was revived in April 1954. A prominent South Carolina woman who had been coming to Pawley's for twenty years brought her children and grandchildren that month for a visit.

Arriving late on a Thursday afternoon, the entire family went to look at the ocean. The grandmother was standing on the raised walkway that led from her home to the top of the dunes. As she looked toward the beach she saw a man of

145

medium build walking northward along the water's edge. He was dressed in gray from head to toe, and he strode along swinging his arms. She watched the man look up at the dunes where she stood and thought at first that he must belong to her party.

Then he became less and less distinct. In her amazement she called out to her family, "Look at that man. He's disappearing!" In a moment what had been a man became a grayish blur. Then even that was gone. Where he had stood there was nothing. He had disappeared before the others realized he was there.

The following day was a miserable one. Vicious winds lashed at the little island and for twenty-four hours weather bulletins predicted possible tornado damage along the coast.

There are numerous Gray Man stories. A recent graphic account comes from a young Georgetown automobile dealer named Bill Collins. His family has owned a home on the Island since he was born.

This pleasant, down-to-earth young man had treated the story of the Gray Man with amused skepticism all his life. He does so no longer.

Just before hurricane Hazel struck, Collins and his wife were staying at the island while he waited to go into military service.

"Just before dusk," Collins says, "I went down to our lookout, a small wooden deck which was perched on top of the dunes and connected by a boardwalk to our house. As I stood there I saw someone walking along the beach. I was curious because there are so few people on the island in October.

"When the person coming toward me got in close focus he simply vanished. I went down to the beach and searched, but there was no sign of a living soul. What puzzled me was the fact that

146

because of the high dunes there was no way for anyone to get off the beach without my seeing him. My wife was amazed when I went back and told her about it.

"About a week later we were all awakened one morning at five o'clock by a loud, insistent pounding on the front door. When I opened it an elderly man stood there dressed in old clothes. He told me the Red Cross had asked him to warn everyone to leave the island. Within an hour we were gone. But the funny part of it is that I had never seen the old fellow before nor have I ever seen him again.

"I asked some of our friends about him and no

It was on this stretch of beach that the Gray Man w

one seemed to know what I was talking about. They had never seen him. Pawley's is just like a small town where everybody knows everybody else, if not by name at least by sight. But I've never been able to find anyone who was warned by or even saw this old man.

"Soon after we left the island, Hazel hit. When we returned after the storm our lookout was gone. Houses had been washed away within a block of us and dunes 30 feet high had disappeared. We could hardly believe it when we found our own house untouched. The TV antenna hadn't even blown down. Beach towels my wife had left hanging on the porch to dry were

)54 to warn of hurricane Hazel.

still right where she had left them. That's part of the Gray Man legend—that no harm comes to those who see him."

"I've been ribbed a lot about this story, you know," adds Collins, smiling wryly, "but it actually happened just the way I've told it."

Who is the Gray Man and why does he walk the beach at Pawley's Island before a storm? There are many stories of his origin. The first originated, we are told, in 1822 before the calamitous storm which cost so many lives.

At this time North Inlet below Pawley's Island was a popular resort with the population of a small town. Many plantation owners had summer homes here. The pretty daughter of one of them was spending the summer with her father and sisters when she received word that her fiancé, who had been abroad for two years, would soon be home.

The young man would stop to pay his respects to his own family at their house on Pawley's Island first and then ride on to North Inlet. The happy girl directed the servants to prepare his favorite dishes for a welcoming dinner and the house was adorned with flowers and greenery.

Meantime, her suitor and his Negro servant were galloping along the Pawley's Island strand. The young man was in high spirits and gaily challenged his companion to a race. Near Middleton Pond he saw a short cut through a marshy area and decided to take it. But his horse stumbled and he pitched headlong into the mire.

When he tried to get to his feet he found himself only sinking deeper into the mud. In a matter of minutes he and his horse were floundering desperately in the quicksand. The Negro servant tried to throw his bridle to his master but the reins were too short. He searched for a pole or a long branch but could find nothing. In an agony

147

of helplessness he watched his young master and his horse sink beneath the sand.

The young girl was inconsolable. In her grief she walked endlessly along the strand. One afternoon when a Northeast wind blew a fine spray across the beach she saw the figure of a man standing looking out over the water. He was dressed in gray and as she approached him and he became more distinct, her heart began to pound violently. She was only a few feet from him and now she was certain it was her dead lover who stood before her. Then a mist seemed to swirl up from the sea and wrap itself about him. He was gone.

When she told her family of the occurrence, they looked at each other sadly. They could only believe that the shock of her loss was beginning to affect her mind.

That night she had a dream so frighteningly vivid that she ran to her father's room for comfort. She had dreamed she was in a tiny boat tossed to and fro by heavy seas. All about her floated pieces of wreckage. And on a high sand dune, which she was helpless to reach, stood her lover beckoning her toward him.

The next day the girl's father decided to carry his daughter to a renowned Charleston physician. The entire family accompanied them. Within hours after they had left the Inlet tragedy struck. A savage hurricane swooped down upon the coast. For two days the storm raged like a monster run amuck.

When it was finally over news came that almost the entire population of North Inlet had perished. Homes were swept out to sea before the inhabitants were able to escape. The savage storm of 1822 had come and gone and the disaster would be remembered for many a year.

By now the fortunate young lady realized that the appearance of her lover and the dream had saved her life as well as the lives of the members of her family. Resigned at last to the loss of her fiance, she became her normal self again. Although this took place over a century ago many of the natives of the island are convinced the Gray Man still returns.

If you should happen to be walking along the strand and encounter a misty figure dressed in gray—remember, he brings a warning.

Tsali, the Cherokee Brave

He gave his life for his people, and his ghost still walks the mountain peaks which were once his home

When the harvest moon pours its rays over the mist shrouded peaks of the Great Smoky Mountains, men swear they see the ghostly figure of an Indian striding the leafy trails or silhouetted for an instant against the sky as though gazing across the deep shadowed valleys.

Thus read a dispatch of the Associated Press on August 3, 1940. The story appeared in the *Charlotte Observer* and other North Carolina newspapers on the wire service.

Few people knew the Indian's name. It was Tsali. He had been a brave in the powerful Cherokee nation a century before. His home was on the Little Tennessee River not far from the village of Echota, a Cherokee capital near the North Carolina-Tennessee border where the mountains thrust themselves 6,000 feet up into the sky. It is here that the spirit of Tsali roams. And those of his people who dwell there today do so only because of him.

The ghost of Tsali has been seen now for more than a hundred years. No one can say when it first appeared or how often it has been seen. But his story is part of a sad and ugly chapter in our history.

In Tsali's time the Cherokee nation extended across and beyond the great mountains. The boundaries had been set in war with the Powha-tan, Monacan, Tuscarora, Catawba, Creek, Chickasaw, and Shawano. After the defeat of the Creek and Shawano, the Cherokee lands extended from upper Georgia to the Ohio River and included hunting grounds in Kentucky.

But from the East came white settlers pushing steadily farther into the Cherokee territory. In 1777, just a year after the Declaration of Independence was signed, the North Carolina legislature offered a bounty of land to able bodied men who would fight the Cherokee. Of course, this land was to come from the Indians.

At that time Tennessee was still part of North Carolina. Among the men who came forward to fight the Indians was Colonel John Sevier. (Later he led his men in a vital victory over the British at King's Mountain.) Another young man named Andrew Jackson also joined the campaign. When peace finally came again and treaties were signed, the Cherokees saw much of their land taken away.

But it wasn't the desire for farm land or the settlers moving West that finally sounded the death knell of the Cherokee nation. Its fate was sealed the day an Indian boy found a yellow

149

stone in a creek near the present site of Dahlonega, Georgia. His mother polished it and showed it to a white trader. The "stone" was gold.

Like a pestilence the cry spread: "There's gold on the Cherokee land!"

Old treaties were forgotten and a new treaty was signed in 1817 and approved by President James Monroe. It provided for removing the Cherokee from the Great Smoky Mountains to the Territory of Oklahoma. After all, the Cherokee didn't "need" gold and there was other land out beyond the Mississippi where they could hunt.

Rage swept the Cherokee nation. War drums echoed across haze filled valleys. Then the white men, faced by certain conflict, backed down and years of bickering followed. At last they agreed to pay the Cherokees five million dollars for their land—the land of the sky.

It was a warm spring day in May of 1838 when General Winfield Scott marched into Cherokee country at the head of seven thousand troops. He delivered an ultimatum to the Cherokee chiefs. They and their people must "move West before the new moon."

The soldiers set about building stockades and rounding up Indians. Cattle were shot. Families were seized, many while they were eating. Some were not even given time to gather up their possessions. What was to be an orderly move turned into a debacle. Perhaps it was a miscarriage of orders, or maybe lower ranking officers who hated the Indians abused their authority—who can say? But the effect was disastrous.

By the time the first group of Indians reached the banks of the Mississippi there was ice in the river. There were no shelters, no blankets. The soldiers didn't provide them. Before the Indians reached Oklahoma four thousand of them were dead. It was one of the most shameful episodes in American history.

150

When the move westward started, Tsali was living in the Ocono Luftee Valley with his wife, three children, and a brother. Three soldiers seized Tsali as he worked in a field near his home. He and his family were led down the mountain to a stockade. The soldiers planned to keep them there until they had rounded up all the Indians. Then they would herd them toward Oklahoma.

As the group made their way along the trail one of the soldiers prodded Tsali's wife to walk faster. Tsali called out something in the Cherokee tongue to his sons and they attacked the guards. In the scuffle a rifle went off and one of the soldiers fell dead. The others ran.

Tsali and his family fled back into the high mountains. The mountains were their home and they would not leave them. Other Cherokee families were doing the same. But the guards reported that Tsali had killed a soldier and General Scott was determined not to let any Indian who killed a white man go free.

The General knew it would cost him many men to capture Tsali among the mountains and that the remaining Cherokees would fight to the death before allowing themselves to be taken.

So Scott called on a white trader named William Thomas to find Tsali. The General must have felt that Tsali had a sense of honor for he made him an offer:

"Tell Tsali that if he will come down and give himself up the rest of his people can stay in the great mountains."

Thomas was a trusted trader and friend of the Indians. They took him to Tsali.

It was one life for a thousand. If Tsali gave himself up the General would leave the mountains in peace. The Indians who had escaped the troops would be free to live in the Smokies forever. The chief of the white man's army would pledge this.

Tasli accepted the offer and came down from the mountains. The Indians were left in peace as Scott had promised, but the price was Tsali's life. He was shot by a firing squad.

It was a score of years before troops again forced their way into the North Carolina mountains. These were blue clad men under Stoneman and they were cutting east through the mountains in an effort to free Union prisoners at Salisbury. The cavalry pickets may have been nervous, for several reported seeing the silhouette of an Indian brave walking along the ridge in the moonlight. They fired but their echoing shots struck nothing.

For a hundred years now there has been peace in the valleys of the Smokies. But if you don't believe that Tsali still strides proudly along the trails, go there when the harvest moon pours its rays on the mist of an autumn night.

Go where there is no highway, where the mountains are high. Watch there for the figure of an Indian silhouetted tall against the sky.

The Ghost

# of Litchfield

**Occupants of Litchfield Plantation have been awakened
many a night by the noisy shade of a former owner**

Litchfield Plantation near All Saints Church near Georgetown, South Carolina, is one of the oldest plantations in the area. It is still beautifully preserved. The ghost of Litchfield who returns to haunt it is one of its former owners. He was a doctor who lived and died here before the Civil War. Later owners of the plantation and the Negroes who lived on it have seen him many times.

The wooden gates and the bell post are gone now, replaced by more durable iron. But still told are stories of the kindly doctor who returns to his beloved Litchfield. His visits are made at night, or very occasionally on a dreary, gray day.

When the doctor was alive he would ride up to the plantation gate on a handsome bay and strike the bell, which had no clapper, with the handle of his riding crop. The doctor kept the gates of his plantation locked. But nearby lived a gatekeeper whose responsibility it was to hear the bell and let him in. Sometimes the gatekeeper would slip away on a visit to a neighboring plantation. When this happened the tired doctor would beat the bell furiously and no one would answer.

He would finally tie his horse to the bell post, climb over a split log fence, and walk down the long avenue of oaks to the house. After late calls he would use the small, private stairway to his room to avoid disturbing the family.

Long after the doctor's death owners of Litchfield would hear the clanging of the bell at all hours of the night as it did when the doctor returned from his calls. Sometimes he would suddenly appear in the house or on the dark little back stairs. But most often he would make his presence known by the clamorous ringing of the bell. Finally, one owner decided he would have his slumbers disturbed no longer. He ordered the bell removed.

He made no secret of the fact that he didn't care how often the good doctor returned but he was tired of being waked up in the dead of night by the bell at the gate.

If you should pass Litchfield late at night and see a bay tethered there in the shadows—you may be sure the doctor has come home again.

City

of

Death

A courageous doctor finally met the shapeless evil that prowled the streets of the stricken city

The port town of Nassau was an exciting, polyglot place in the summer of 1862. There were swaggering blockade runner captains with more money in their pockets than a governor could earn in a year. There were boisterous free Negroes, and there were the islanders themselves who as far back as anyone could remember had earned an unsavory livelihood from pillaging the wrecks washed up on their shores.

It was the last of August when something unseen and full of horror left the island with the crew of the steamer *Kate*, bound for the port of Wilmington, North Carolina. Even if the sailors

155

had been celebrating less heavily before their departure they could hardly have been aware of their fearsome stowaway that was soon to bring tragedy to the people of Wilmington.

The dead might have described it better for us than those fortunate enough to escape. But perhaps we may come to know its gruesome presence through the eyes of a man who during that ill-fated month of September was still alive.

Dr. James H. Dickson, shoulders bent from exhaustion, closed the door of the small house which looked out over the waterfront of the Wilmington harbor. The child he had been treating for several days lay dead in the tiny room he had just left. And as in so many other cases he had visited during the past week, he had been helpless to combat the relentless torment of the yellow fever that had killed his patient.

The disease was a new one to all Wilmington physicians. Municipal authorities were helpless and the country people, fearful of the dread fever, no longer sent in supplies.

Skilled physician that he was, Dickson went endlessly on his rounds, often to the bedside of close friends, only to watch them die. The socially prominent and the humble poor alike tossed, suffered, and went out by the same door, while rude funeral carts rumbled in the streets and carried them all to the same destination.

Although heavy hearted over the ravages of the fever, James Dickson was almost equally disturbed over *the rumor*. As the number of deaths mounted the frightened slaves had started whispers of an accompanying horror, a nameless, faceless thing, an embodiment of evil which roamed the deserted streets and carried with it the touch of death.

A pall of black smoke from the burning barrels of tar designed to purify the air hung over the city and obscured the early morning light.

"Truly an infernal setting for an evil spirit, if such existed, at large in this panic stricken city," thought James Dickson. A man of calmness and logic, it was with determination that he shook off his sombre mood. Such superstitious imaginings could only stem from the fears of the illiterate.

At that moment a gust of wind rustled through the bushes at the edge of the street along which he walked and blew choking black billows toward him from one of the tar barrels. He felt something soft like a cloak brush his face. But as he reached out involuntarily to ward it off his hand met empty air. For a moment his throat almost closed with an unaccustomed emotion—fear.

When he recovered himself he searched the bushes but found nothing. He noted only the now still leaves of the trees as his eyes searched for some other living thing.

As he neared the large magnolia tree in his own yard he saw shadows moving by the steps of his house. Nerving himself to walk toward them he recognized a human figure. It was an old man whose whole body was racked by barely suppressed sobs.

Deeply moved, Dickson asked if he could help him.

"Doctor, it's not me. It's my daughter. In God's name, you've got to help her—she has the fever." And so incoherent did he become that Dickson could hardly understand where the old fellow lived.

On the way he gathered that the family's name was Fairly. The girl was their only daughter. Her husband had died a week ago at Sharpsburg. They entered a modest frame house. The mother's face was drawn but controlled as she led them to her daughter's room.

Dickson looked at the slight form of the girl

lying beneath the sheet. She had been hemorrhaging badly and he knew it was already too late. He administered what little comfort he could, proscribed fruit juices although tortured by the knowledge that the family probably couldn't obtain them due to the blockade, and left. By now almost totally exhausted, he went home and threw himself across his bed.

Another day dawned and the doctor's rounds began anew. Here and there as he left a home a member of the family would accompany him to the door and with an air of embarrassment whisper, "Doctor, they say there is something roaming the streets at night. Tell me, have you seen anything?" And the slaves would listen fearfully, the whites of their eyes shining from the darkness along the edges of the hall.

If Dickson had not been so busy his own imagination, spurred on by fatigue, might have run more rampant. But he would not, could not stop although his own frustration and helplessness lashed him at every bedside. At the home of the Lassiters young James followed him to the door and asked, "Is it true that 'The Thing' got Ben Trumbell last night and left him dead in the street without a mark on his body?"

Dickson merely shook his head tiredly without further reply. When he got home that night his head ached miserably but he decided an account must be written of the cases for future record.

He sat alone in his little office at the back of the house slumped over his roll top desk, the window open at his side. He wrote on and on until his fingers felt cramped. By now his entire body ached and he realized that these were the first symptoms of the pestilence. The curtain stirred softly at the window.

By Friday he was unable to make his calls. But again that night, despite his increasing weakness, he wrote one page after another. The handwriting was somewhat less legible but still bold and unflinching. An unusual chill was in the wind for September and it ruffled his papers.

On Saturday night as he sat at his desk it seemed to him the odor of the tar barrels was more pungent than ever. The wind which now began to blow the curtain aside was almost icy. But his face burned so with the fever that he welcomed it—nay, if there was some presence beyond the blackness of the window which could end all this, he sought it.

With all his remaining strength he turned and stared through the now parted curtains. Strangely enough he recognized what he saw there. It was what he had brushed past that night early in the epidemic, The Thing that every man wonders how he will meet.

Now it was to be his companion beneath the black pall of smoke, his dark escort past the blazing barrels of pitch through the silent streets.

In *The Wilmington Journal* of September 29, 1862, an inconspicuous notice appeared. "Dr. James H. Dickson, a physician of the highest character and standing, died here early Sunday morning of yellow fever. Dr. Dickson's death is a great loss to the profession and to the community."

Treasure

Hunt

The fury of battle seemed almost tame to two young officers after their ghostly encounter on Folly Island

In 1908 in Deadwood, South Dakota, a little book was published by a former Union Army officer. Francis M. Moore had served with distinction during the war between the states but the subject of his book was not a narrative of battles. It was an eerie tale of a search for buried treasure on Folly Island near Charleston harbor.

For half a century those who knew the story were sworn to secrecy. In July of 1863 the 62nd Ohio Regiment was part of a Union force under General Gilmore. The men landed on Folly Island in preparation for an attack on the defenses of Charleston harbor. Before the fighting was to start Gilmore ordered the Negroes living on the island removed and provided a steamer to take them to Port Royal.

A young lieutenant named Yokum, who was supervising one of the details, walked up to a ramshackle cabin occupied by an old Negro woman and a child. When he informed her she would have to leave the island she protested vehemently. The lieutenant, trying to be as kind as possible, sat on the porch and listened to her talk while the child brought him a drink of spring water in a gourd.

The Negress told Yokum how her family had lived in the cabin while pirates still roamed the Carolina coast. Judging that her age must be close to a hundred, he became convinced she was telling the truth as her story appeared to be from first hand experience.

When she mentioned buried treasure the words cut through the oppressive July heat and aroused a spark of interest in the young officer.

"Six chests of gold, silver and jewels were carried ashore by the pirates. They dug a hole for it between dem two big oaks." And she pointed a finger as gnarled as the trees themselves. Her voice dropped almost to a whisper as she told how the frightened Negroes had watched.

As the last chest was lowered into the hole the leader of the buccaneers suddenly stabbed one of his men in the back and tumbled him into the opening. Quickly the other pirates shoveled sand over the body and soon they had vanished back to the sea from whence they had come.

It was not long before a large ship appeared on the horizon, apparently in search of the pirates. From her description Lieutenant Yokum guessed that it might have been a British man of war.

He was now intensely interested.

"I suppose the treasure has been dug up long since?" he asked with only a trace of hope in his voice.

"No suh, no suh. Who gonna go near dat place? Dat pirate he watch over dem chests even do' he dead." And the old woman fell silent, looking out toward the sea. Yokum helped her carry her few belongings down to the boat and she and the child boarded it along with the other Negroes.

That night shortly before twelve o'clock two officers of the 62nd Ohio, each equipped with a shovel, disappeared over the sand dunes. Yokum and his friend, Lieutenant Hatcher, had no trouble finding the giant live oaks which grew a short distance from the Negro cabin. They were shrouded with Spanish moss and so much taller than the other trees on the narrow strip of land that they stood out conspicuously.

As they neared their goal the tops of the trees began to rustle and stir although there was no breeze and the air hung still and heavy with heat.

Taking their bearings and choosing a site directly between the two oaks, which were about twenty feet apart, the men began to dig. There was a flash of lightning and Yokum looked up at the sky for signs of a summer thunderstorm. To his surprise no distant roll of thunder followed. Hatcher pointed to the tops of the trees now swaying and writhing as if buffeted by a strong wind.

They raised their shovels and resumed digging. The sand which the wind swept against their faces and bare torsos stung like thousands of tiny needles. But they continued to dig. By now the darkness was illuminated by numerous flashes of lightning and at times they could see each other as plainly as if it were day.

Then a flash came which seemed to last for several seconds. The area where they dug became bright as noonday. At that moment a shattering realization came to both men.

They were not alone.

There was someone or something standing there beside them. Was it human? The figure was one that neither of them would ever be able to forget. It was clearly that of a pirate.

Yokum and Hatcher waited for no introduction. They fled in panic over the dunes and back toward their camp. When they reached its safety the two men swore to each other that they would not tell of their experience.

The following day the 62nd attacked Morris Island. Hatcher and Yokum fought with a calmness and valor that astonished their comrades. Perhaps they did so with a sense of relief that their enemies were mere mortals. Then came the assault on Fort Wagner and Fort Fisher. Both men were decorated for bravery.

Even at the end of the war the story of that night on the beach remained untold. A few years later Hatcher had died and Yokum had gone out West to make his home.

It was not until fifty years after the war that Yokum related their experience at a veterans' reunion. It was recorded by his friend, Francis M. Moore, and should make interesting reading for all who are tempted to wrest buried treasure from its owners!

House of the Opening Door

Why did the door open each night without benefit of human hand? Few cared to stay long enough to find out

A house is more than just its timbers. It is the lives which have been lived there, the deeds which have been done within its walls. There are houses which finally can only be at home in hell itself. If you glimpse one on your travels do not tarry. It may prove a trap of terror, a passport to the damned.

But the couple who sat in their ancient auto looking hopefully at the gaunt structure rising before them did not think of these things. If they had been told they might not have cared. For they were desperate. All John and Harriet West could think of was that they had at last found shelter for themselves and their four children.

Harriet gazed at the tangle of dead vines hanging over the porch, writhing at the touch of the wind. And she was foolish enough to picture clematis growing in their place. Devil's Walking Stick might have thrived on this God-forsaken spot—but flowers . . . never.

John's eyes looked beyond the grotesque, broken trees which must once have been giants and daydreamed of an apple orchard. What did these two outsiders care for the strange expressions on the faces of the North Carolina mountain people whom they had stopped to ask the way to the house? It was enough for them that it had four walls and a roof.

Harriet and John West stood in the front yard of the place they expected to call home, their coats whipped around them by the wind, two silhouettes in the falling dusk. Behind them their children peered curiously from the car windows, quiet now that the journey was over. Then the entire family began the work of unloading the small canvas covered trailer which held their meager household goods.

That night the children were exhausted and needed no urging to go to their floor pallets. Soon they were slumbering soundly.

162

John and his wife worked on. He had discovered a few boards at the back of the house, the last of a tumbled down shed, and chopped some wood which hissed and crackled in the big stone fireplace. Shortly before midnight they pulled their chairs close to the hearth and began to talk of their plans for fixing up their new home.

The fire cast strange shadows on the broken plaster of the walls. The vines scraped eerily as the wind blew them back and forth against the outside of the house. The Wests were too absorbed to notice either.

Then they both started. Above the steady wail of the wind came an earsplitting sound. It was the shriek of a train whistle echoing and re-echoing through the night. Hardly a mile from where the house stood, a stretch of railroad track ran through a narrow gap between two hills. Before the train entered the straightaway beyond the gap its engineer blew a long shrill blast of the whistle which was answered and echoed back and forth all down the corridor formed by the hills.

It was not a comforting thing to hear and the Wests looked at each other, wordlessly waiting for what might follow. When it came they were still unprepared. At the far end of the room was a door leading to the long ell which ran back of the two story part of the house. Back there had originally been a kitchen and small servant's room. The Wests had decided to close this room off, keeping it as a storage place for farm tools, and use only the front part of the house.

But someone or something had decided differently. Something that was not to be closed in or perhaps kept out. As the man and woman watched, frozen with apprehension, the knob on the door seemed to turn slowly. They heard the latch click and then a crack appeared between the door and the door jamb. So slight it was that one at first might only have imagined it to be there. But the streak of velvety blackness widened with horrifying deliberation until at last the entire black maw of the door gaped at the pair sitting before the fire.

For a long moment neither moved. Then came a sharp crash as if some large object had been hurled savagely through the air against the wall in the pitch black storage room.

John West jumped to his feet, grasped a candle and hesitating only for a moment at the door of the room disappeared inside it. Harriet watched as the flickering candle stretched faltering fingers of light over the walls and across the floor. There was no living thing to be seen. The room was empty and everything seemed undisturbed. Almost everything, that is. On the floor lay a large scythe—its sharp, wickedly curved blade shining in the semi-darkness.

John West picked it up quickly and hung it back on the wall, then turned to his wife:

"Well, you can see for yourself it was nothing. Only the scythe falling from the wall. We're both tired and jumpy. Tomorrow you won't give an old door with a loose catch a thought."

Harriet West looked at her husband, her eyes still frightened. But she said nothing. It was now after midnight, and they went on to bed. Soon Harriet was asleep, but not her husband. He knew he had hung the scythe securely over hooks on the wall of the storage room and go over it as he would in his mind he knew of no way it could have fallen to the floor—particularly since it had come to rest fully ten feet from where he had hung it.

The next day the opening door and the chilling fear which had accompanied it seemed like only a bad dream to be dissipated by the sunlight. And only now and then did a nagging uneasiness about the scythe touch the mind of John

West as he busied himself with minor repairs to the wretched, rundown old house. The latch of the door to the storage room appeared to be more than secure. In fact it was even a bit difficult to open, being rusty from years of disuse.

Shortly after supper the children went to bed exhausted from exploring every nook and cranny of the house and the land around it.

John and Harriet West were tired, too. But neither would admit to it, nor to the fact that they were both waiting. For a while they talked. Then they were too tired even for that. Finally Harriet's head came to rest on her husband's shoulder. By now it was almost midnight.

Then the sound they had been waiting for came. Louder, eerier than ever the scream of the train's whistle broke the stillness and behind it came the rumble, rumble, rumble of the freight cars rushing down the straightaway. Both stared tensely at the door and as they watched it began to open once again. Harriet gripped John's hand, her face white with fear. The door hung wide on its hinges. Now from somewhere in the blackness of the room beyond came a loud crash.

John West ran toward the door with Harriet close behind him. There in the light of the candle lay the scythe on the floor just as it had been the night before. This time when he picked it up he found to his horror that the blade bore a rusty—or was it reddish?—stain. It had struck the floor with such force that the board on which it rested was scarred.

As he passed his fingers over the mark the board moved and he saw that it was quite loose. So loose that he could easily lift it. Peering under it, John West saw to his surprise an old metal box. The box was wedged in so tightly that it was only with the help of his crowbar that West managed to pry it out. Taking the box into the

other room in front of the fire, they both worked at the lock. Finally, John struck it with the crowbar and the lock sprang open.

What John and Harriet were to find inside that box was to change their whole lives. It was a turning point they would never be able to forget or to explain.

The lid of the box still held fast to its secret. John worked the crowbar around its edge impatiently until all at once it gave way, flying back with such suddenness that the contents of the box spilled over onto the floor. The pair gasped with amazement. For a moment both were speechless. Stacked inside the box and spilling over onto the floor around it was more money than they had ever seen in their lives.

This was no pirate's treasure of gold doubloons, but musty old bills—currency which must have been stacked away long years before. Sitting on the floor they counted the money a half dozen times, their hands shaking with excitement, before they realized that they had discovered well over ten thousand dollars.

They talked until the early hours of the dawn of how they would spend their find, before at last they fell asleep. They would buy a small farm, they would have a cow so the children could have all the milk they wanted. Harriet would be able to get some chickens and John could buy a horse with which to plow.

But however the Wests would eventually spend their treasure, one thing was certain. They would never spend another night listening for the shriek of the train and waiting in dread for the ell door to open. By early the next afternoon the house was again alone with its secrets. The Wests were gone.

As the years went by an occasional family would stay in the house on the hill for a few nights and leave. Even tramps were not brave enough to spend more than a night or two in the "house of the opening door."

The strange story of the house and its door spread until it reached the ears of a young engineer. He was able to interest a group in solving the mystery and they came with their tape measures and their instruments to examine the house and surrounding area with scientific thoroughness. For two weeks they stayed, watching as the door opened. They were convinced that there is nothing in the world that will not allow itself to be measured and categorized.

Despite their air of skepticism more than one felt a strange sense of foreboding when midnight approached. One slipped a loaded pistol into his pocket while his friends laughed at his precaution.

As each midnight drew near the blasts of the train whistle pierced the air and rebounded be-

tween the hills. Then the door would swing open slowly, finally to rest against the wall. There was certainly a scientific explanation, the men believed, and so they studied and argued over the problem, taking voluminous notes and sitting before the fire night after night. Finally they decided they had solved the mystery. This is what they wrote in their report:

The mountains of Western North Carolina are the oldest in the world. At one time they stretched across what is now the Pacific Ocean, to join this country with Japan. In these old, old mountains are many peculiar geologic formations—strange strata of rock which are found in few other mountain ranges. We would call attention to the fact that on many of the mountain tops there are found bold flowing springs.

"The structure locally known as the House of the Opening Door rests on a hill of almost solid rock, the soil in some places a few feet thick, and in others only scant inches. The midnight train which passes through every night at almost the same time is the heaviest freight going over this route. It has a clear track, for there are no other trains passing near this time, and its rate of speed is unchecked. The terrific weight and velocity of this train jars a certain stratum of rock as it makes the curve just before reaching the straight sweep in to the water tank at the station. By an unusual, perhaps remarkable coincidence, the House of the Opening Door rests on the same vein and stratum of rock and the vibrations are carried from one point to the other.

"The opening door has been measured very carefully and we find that it does not hang exactly true, so the trembling shock imparted to the layer of rock by the heavy train is carried in successive waves to the stout foundation under that part of the house. The trembling is sufficient to swing the door."

Thus was the mystery of the opening door disposed of scientifically.

When the natives heard the results of the report they merely shook their heads. It might be that the men with the "book larnin'" had discovered the door's secret, but no one cared to stay in the house overnight to find out.

Then an old man and his son who had been burned out of their own home decided they would spend a night in the house to find out whether they wanted to move in.

They awoke just in time to see the door swing open and hear a noise like the shuffling of feet in the other room. Then from the blackness of the open doorway something shiny came hurtling through the air and landed perilously close to the younger man's head. Both father and son jumped up and fled out into the night.

A year later a group of children wandered near the house in play. One of the girls peeked through a window heavy with cobwebs and there in the middle of the room in a streak of sunlight stood a ragged old man. Under one arm he cradled something which might have been a box and in his other hand he held a knife which he plunged fiercely into the air. The child screamed and the old man vanished.

For a long time now the house has stood empty. Its appearance grows more grim year by year. But still it waits on its lonely hill in western North Carolina with the broken off trees looming like lost souls around it. If you care to spend the night there you have the reassuring report of the engineers.

But local people say it would do no good to nail the door shut or plaster over it for "what comes through that door will not be shut out or closed in. When the time comes it will be there—door or no door."

The Ghosts of Hagley

On a moonlit night in 1918 a Georgetown man learned that phantoms still walk the earth

Some years back Eugene F. LaBruce, member of a prominent Georgetown, South Carolina family, gave the following account of his experience with the "Ghosts of Hagley."

It was in the summer of 1918 that I underwent an experience destined to change all of my preconceived ideas about the spirit world . . . An experience which convinced me beyond the shadow of a doubt that ghosts do walk the earth.

I never recall having any fear of ghosts and like most people thought they were merely products of an overwrought imagination. But the peculiar events of that summer demonstrated very plainly that I was wrong.

At the time, I was engaged in carrying passengers between Pawley's Island and the ferry landing of Hagley. Between the Island and the landing was a sandy road several miles long. Using a large automobile, I would make the trip a number of times during the day. Often a party of young people who worked in Georgetown would hire a gasoline launch after the ferry had made its last trip and I would meet them at Hagley about a quarter of eleven.

One night when I reached the ferry landing early I decided to stretch out on a piece of canvas on the wharf and get a little rest before the boat from Georgetown arrived. The moon shone brightly, flooding the landscape with its soft light, and every object was plainly visible. It was a peaceful scene and a few minutes later I had drifted off to sleep.

The dream that came to me that night was so vivid that I can remember every detail to this day.

I was standing with a crowd of people in front of a little church near the wharf. A wedding was in progress and it seemed that we were waiting for the bride and groom to emerge from the front door. Everyone wore clothing typical of the Civil War period, and I gathered that peace had just been declared. After a short while the bridal party appeared on the church porch. I stared at the newly married couple standing there in the moonlight and noticed that the bride was a striking brunette, and the groom a handsome, finely proportioned blond. Both were of the landed gentry class, I imagined.

As the crowd surged toward the porch a man dressed in Confederate uniform dashed up to the clearing astride a horse that had evidently been running at top speed for hours. The figure dismounted and ran toward the place where the bride and groom stood. When he reached the couple the bride uttered a little cry and said, "It is too late, I have just been married!"

The soldier stood frozen and listened like a man in a trance while the woman explained that she had waited three years, and believing that he had been killed in battle had finally consented to marry one of her former beaus.

The soldier then turned to the groom and said, without show of emotion, "Then I will fade out of the picture—it is the only solution." And he turned to leave. But the groom started after him. "No! If it must be one of us, I will be the one."

Followed by the bride and groom the soldier

made for the wharf. When he reached the end of the pier he jumped off and disappeared. Without a second's hesitation, the woman in white followed him and then the groom.

Everyone was in a turmoil. Boats were launched, the stronger swimmers among the men jumped into the water and a score of men were calling orders in rapid succession. A severe gale had begun blowing from the west lashing the waves against the bank. The search for the bodies was still under way when I awoke, shivering with excitement.

168

I rubbed my eyes and looked about me. The church had disappeared and the crowd of men and women had vanished. It scarcely seemed like a dream, I had witnessed the entire train of events so clearly and with such detail. But it must have been for I was back on the wharf. Only one thing had changed. I was no longer alone.

For as I turned my head I saw two figures standing only a few feet away. And to my amazement they were dressed like the people in my dream, the woman resembling the bride and the man, the groom!

"This is nonsense," I assured myself. "The boat has come and gone and the passengers are somewhere nearby. These two are trying to play a trick on me." So I said, most politely, "Will you tell me who you are? If you are waiting to go to Pawley's I have the automobile ready."

They did not answer so I tried again. Neither deigned to reply, but turned around and strolled off the dock. This made me angry and I called out, "You better stop this foolishness and tell me who you are, for I will find out soon enough."

But the couple kept walking slowly away from me and seemed to be whispering to each other. Then I became really frightened and started to imagine all sorts of weird things. Could some mysterious force have carried me back through the years to the time of the Civil War? I tried to recall the history of this area but couldn't remember ever hearing of a church at Hagley, reading of such an incident or hearing a similar story told. Why, then, should I have this dream?

I was still trying to answer these questions when the couple disappeared. I had been watching them intently and was sure they had no opportunity to slip into the woods. They had simply melted away without a trace.

Scarcely had I collected my wits when the motor boat arrived with its passengers. I tried my best to conceal my agitation as they followed me to the automobile and we were soon ploughing along the sandy roadbed headed for the beach. The car was in second gear traveling at about twenty miles an hour when I saw two figures step out into the road directly in front of the machine. With no clearance on either side of the car there was nothing to do but slam on the brakes.

So sudden was the stop that my passengers were thrown violently against each other and started calling, "What are you trying to do, throw us out of the car?"

Cold perspiration broke out on my face. The figures were still in the road walking arm in arm and there was the brunette bride of my dream and the handsome groom. There was no mistaking their features or the costumes. They did not even throw a glance in the direction of the car and I was sure no living beings could have failed to notice the automobile bearing down upon them.

"Here are my ghosts again," I said to myself. "Perhaps I am going mad."

"What's the matter?" yelled a young man in a sporty blue coat "Have you lost your voice? That was a fine trick."

"Oh, I just thought I would throw you and your girl friend together," I replied. When I looked back at the road the figures were gone. I was afraid the girl at my side would notice my agitation but she seemed absorbed in her own thoughts.

When we reached the beach my passengers alighted—all except the girl who was seated next to me. She seemed reluctant to leave and when her companions called to her she said, "All of you run along, I want to talk to Eugene a while." So they laughed but moved on down the beach.

The girl turned to me. "Eugene, I want you to tell me why you stopped the car so suddenly by the ferry landing."

"Oh, I just wanted to have a little fun," I replied trying to stick to my original story.

"You needn't tell me that. I know why you stopped."

My heart was beating faster and faster. Perhaps this young woman had seen the same figures. In this case nothing was the matter with my mind and probably two real ghosts had appeared.

"Why don't you believe me?" I countered.

"Because," and she averted her eyes, "you know you saw a man and a woman in the road."

"If we did, no one else in the car saw them," I asserted.

"That makes no difference. I saw them and you did, too, or you would never have slammed on brakes as you did."

There was no use pretending any longer. "Yes, I saw them," I said evenly, "and I barely missed killing them at that." I knew that was not an accurate statement for the car would probably not have injured the couple a bit. They would have dissolved in front of my eyes. But I was determined not to frighten the girl.

"But who were they, Eugene?" she persisted. "I never remember seeing them around here before, and did you notice those odd old fashioned clothes they wore?"

"Perhaps strangers out for a stroll, waiting to meet another car," I told the eager questioner.

But I knew better. I had seen two ghosts—the real thing. The fact that this girl and I had both seen the same apparitions left no doubt in my mind that spirits do exist and that we had been granted a rare privilege.

For all I know the beautiful bride and her groom may still stroll the wooded paths around the ferry landing at Hagley on bright moonlight nights.

Return from the Dead

A good friend in life came back from the grave to reproach Alexander Hostler for a horrible mistake

Many stories have been written about old graveyards and countless legends have sprung up around them. One of these stories is still told in connection with the graveyard which lies south of historic St. James Episcopal Church in Wilmington, North Carolina, and the testimony put in writing is worth retelling. The facts were given by the late Colonel James G. Burr in a lecture which he delivered in the Wilmington Opera House on February 3, 1890.

Spring came very early that March of 1810 in Wilmington, North Carolina, but its loveliness passed unnoticed by Alexander Hostler. So grieved was Hostler by the death of his intimate friend, Samuel Jocelyn, that he shut himself up in his library wishing only to be alone.

To walk the streets and greet mutual friends or frequent the places which he and Samuel had enjoyed together was an almost unbearable experience. Son of a distinguished Wilmington lawyer, Jocelyn had been a most promising and charming young man. His death in an accident a few days before had greatly affected Hostler.

As Hostler sat alone in his library two days after the funeral he was startled from his brooding by the sudden appearance of a figure before him. To his astonishment he recognized his friend Jocelyn, who said to him, "How could you let me be buried when I was not yet dead?"

"Not dead?" exclaimed the horror stricken Alexander.

"No, I was not," replied Samuel. "Open my coffin and you will see that I am not lying on my back in the position in which you placed me." And the figure vanished.

171

Hostler, though greatly disturbed, believed that he must be the victim of a delusion brought on by the extreme shock and grief which he had suffered. He made every effort to rationalize his experience.

The next evening he sat again in his study. Scribbling away with a quill pen at his desk, he forced himself to perform the painful task of writing an account of Samuel's death to friends living some distance away.

He had been writing not more than half an hour when he was seized by an overwhelming prescience that something inexplicable was about to occur. Glancing up from his desk he was aghast to find the apparition of Jocelyn standing only a few feet away as it had on the previous evening. Again the ghost entreated him to open the coffin and again it vanished.

Hostler was much upset and when he closeted himself alone in his room on the following evening, he sat at his desk with considerable apprehension. It was less than an hour before he realized that he was not alone. There at his elbow stood the apparition this time beseeching him even more pitifully.

He could stand it no longer. His rationalizations were of no use to him and his state of mind was such that he determined to seek out his friend Louis Toomer that very night and ask for his help.

The two men talked until nearly midnight. Greatly concerned over Hostler's condition, Toomer tried his utmost to reassure him but his efforts were of no avail. Hostler's distressed mien and haggard appearance finally convinced Toomer that nothing would satisfy him but the opening of Jocelyn's grave.

So he consented to assist in the grisly task and they began to lay their plans. The disinterment must be done at night in order that they might accomplish it in the strictest secrecy. Toomer was to bring the shovels and enter the cemetery from the rear while Hostler was to provide a lantern. They agreed to meet at Jocelyn's grave at 11:30 the following evening.

The appointed night was overcast and only occasionally did the waning moon show itself from behind the shifting clouds. The graveyard was pitch dark when the men, talking in low tones, began their undertaking. Before long the moon peered down upon the gravediggers and cast its eerie glow on the headstones around them.

They dug silently on until with a thud Hostler's shovel struck the top of the coffin. Carefully they uncovered it and raised the lid. Both men stooped over it, turning the light of the lantern full upon the contents of the coffin. With a strangled cry Hostler threw his arm across his face.

There lay the body—face downward! In truth, young Samuel Jocelyn had been buried alive.

In order that as little publicity as possible might be given the tragic error both Hostler and Toomer made no general mention of their discovery. But Hostler confided in Colonel Burr's mother who was his near relative and Toomer told the facts of the disinterment in the presence of another venerable lady, Mrs. C. G. Kennedy, who put his statement in writing for Colonel Burr.

There have been many theories as to how such a thing could have happened. Jocelyn had been thrown from his horse while riding and was picked up and carried to his home in a comatose condition. Then presumably dead, the body remained in the home for two days before it was interred in St. James churchyard. A newspaper writer in 1926 wrote:

"The assumption is that the fall from the horse brought on a state of catalepsy with accompanying muscular rigidity convincing everyone that the youth was dead."

Whatever the medical explanation for this appearance of death which resulted in the burial of a living man, the apparition itself is even more beyond our realm of understanding.

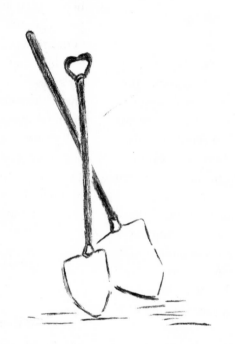

Whistle While You Haunt

The young man died a painful, lingering death, but he often returns to whistle his favorite melody

A cold, steady downpour of rain beat upon the stagecoach as it bumped and jerked along the cobblestone streets of Charleston. It was the year 1786 and for homesick Joseph Ladd Brown of Rhode Island, the first view of the city in which he was to spend the balance of his life was a dismal one.

He had chosen to settle in Charleston for reasons of health. But the night he had selected for his arrival was far from an auspicious omen.

The door to the coach opened and Joseph found the face of the driver thrust close to his own. The man was trying to tell him something above the sound of the storm. They had pulled up before a small tavern and the driver recommended that Joseph find lodging there for the night.

His relief that the trip was over soon fled, for the crowd within was a rowdy one. While the young doctor watched with growing distaste a well dressed man, clearly above the revelers about him, entered the tavern. He made his way to Joseph and introduced himself.

"I am Ralph Isaacs. You appear to be a stranger here and if you will forgive me for saying so, this is not a suitable lodging for a gentleman. Allow me to guide you elsewhere."

Joseph thanked him gratefully and soon the two were on their way in Isaac's own carriage to a quiet, comfortable inn. As they drove along together they found much in common and the young doctor was impressed with Isaac's *savoir faire* and knowledge of the city.

Within a few days Joseph found permanent lodgings in the home of two sisters who were friends of General Nathanial Greene, a business associate of his father.

175

Gradually he began to build up a good medical practice in the city and his ability as a poet, together with his personal charm, combined to make him much sought after. The two elderly ladies became increasingly fond of their young boarder. And each afternoon they found themselves listening for his cheerful whistling as he bounded up the stairs. It was always the same tune—a quaint old English ballad—and when they heard it they knew he was in a high good humor.

Joseph continued to see much of his friend Ralph Isaacs, but more and more Isaac's jealousy over the young doctor's popularity began to cloud their friendship. Ralph Isaacs had never attained the social prominence which was coming to Joseph so readily and his resentment grew.

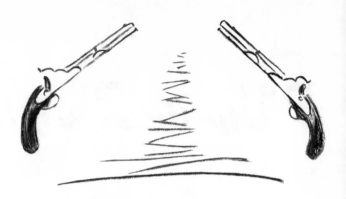

One evening they attended the Shakespearean drama *Richard III* but they were not seated together since seating in theaters at that time was arranged in accordance with one's social standing. The actress, a Miss Barrett, was hopelessly inadequate and spoke her lines so softly that she could scarcely be heard.

On the way home the two men argued over the quality of the performance. And what had begun as a difference of opinion soon ended in a serious quarrel.

Dr. Brown took it upon himself to organize a protest of Isaac's conduct which was printed in the Charleston *Gazette*. In the letter to the newspaper Brown said, "I account it one of the misfortunes of my life that I became intimate with that man."

Isaacs then fired back a bitter reply calling Brown "a self-created doctor and as blasted a scoundrel as ever disgraced humanity."

Brown's friends advised him that it was now a matter of honor which could only be settled by a challenge to a duel. The challenge was readily accepted and the duel was set for the following morning. Actually, Dr. Brown was reluctant to settle the matter in such a manner and wanted to call off the duel, but it was now too late.

Early the next morning the two antagonists examined their guns, stood back to back, paced the agreed upon twenty steps and turned face to face. Brown raised his pistol high and fired straight into the air—then stood motionless and waited. Isaacs was not so merciful. He fired his pistol twice, each time hitting Brown in the legs below the knees. He was determined to cripple the doctor for life.

The wounded young man was carried back to the home of the sisters and for three weeks he lingered between life and death. Physicians were able to do little to alleviate his suffering and finally he died.

But the cheerful ballad which he loved to whistle did not die with him. For it is said that the merry English tune and his bounding footsteps have been heard many times on the stairs of the old home at 59 Church Street.

*These are the stairs
where the doctor's
footsteps and whistling
have been heard.*

The Brown Mountain Lights

Seen and investigated for more than a century, a tantalizing mystery remains unsolved in the mountains of North Carolina

The Brown Mountain Lights are one of the most famous of North Carolina legends. They have been reported a dozen times in newspaper stories. They have been investigated at least twice by the U.S. Geological Survey. And they have attracted the attention of numerous scientists and historians since the German engineer, Gerard William de Brahm, recorded the mysterious lights in the North Carolina mountains in 1771.

"The mountains emit nitrous vapors which are borne by the wind and when laden winds meet each other the niter inflames, sulphurates and deteriorates," said de Brahm. De Brahm was a scientific man and, of course, had a scientific explanation. But the early frontiersman believed that the lights were the spirits of Cherokee and

Catawba warriors slain in an ancient battle on the mountainside.

One thing is certain, the lights do exist. They have been seen from earliest times. They appear at irregular intervals over the top of Brown Mountain—a long, low mountain in the foothills of the Blue Ridge. They move erratically up and down, visible at a distance but vanishing as one climbs the mountain. From Wiseman's View on Linville Mountain the lights can be seen well. They at first appear to be about twice the size of a star as they come over Brown Mountain. Sometimes they have a reddish or blue cast. On dark nights they pop up so thick and fast it's impossible to count them.

Among the scientific investigations which have undertaken from time to time to explain the lights have been two conducted by the U.S. Geological Survey. The first was made in 1913 when the conclusion was reached that the lights, were locomotive headlights from the Catawba Valley south of Brown Mountain. However, three years later in 1916 a great flood that swept through the Catawba Valley knocked out the railroad bridges. It was weeks before the right-of-way could be repaired and the locomotives could once again enter the valley. Roads were also washed out and power lines were down.

But the lights continued to appear as usual. It became apparent that the lights could not be reflections from locomotive or automobile headlights.

The *Guide to the Old North State*, prepared by the W.P.A. in the 1930's, states that the Brown Mountain lights have "puzzled scientists for fifty years." The same story reports sightings of the lights in the days before the Civil War.

Cherokee Indians were familiar with these lights as far back as the year 1200. According to Indian legend, a great battle was fought that year between the Cherokee and Catawba Indians near Brown Mountain. The Cherokees believed that the lights were the spirits of Indian maidens who went on searching through the centuries for their husbands and sweethearts who had died in the battle.

There are innumerable stories of the lights. But perhaps the best description is that the lights are "a troop of candle-bearing ghosts who are destined to march forever back and forth across the mountain."

The lights can be seen from as far away as Blowing Rock or the old Yonahlosse Trail over Grandfather Mountain some fifteen miles from Brown Mountain. At some points closer to Brown Mountain the lights seem large, resembling balls of fire from a Roman candle. Some-

times they may rise to various heights and fade slowly. Others expand as they rise, then burst high in the air like an explosion without sound.

Late in 1919 the question of the Brown Mountain lights was brought to the attention of the Smithsonian Institution and the United States Weather Bureau.

Dr. W. J. Humphries of the Weather Bureau investigated and reported that the Brown Mountain lights were similar to the Andes light of South America. The Andes light and its possible relation to the Brown Mountain lights became the subject of a paper read before the American Meteorological Society in April 1941. In this report Dr. Herbert Lyman represented the lights as a manifestation of the Andes light.

The second U.S. Geological Survey report disposes of the cause of the Brown Mountain lights by saying they are due to the spontaneous combustion of marsh gases. But there are no marshy places on or about Brown Mountain. The report also states that the lights from foxfire would be too feeble to be seen at a distance of several miles.

The report rules out the possibility that the lights are a reflection of mountain moonshine stills. "There are not enough such stills and they probably would not be in sufficiently continuous operation to produce lights in the number and regularity of those seen at Brown Mountain."

St. Elmo's Fire, that electrical phenomenon familiar to sea voyagers, was dismissed by a scientist from the Smithsonian Institution. He stated that St. Elmo's Fire and similar phenomena occurred at the extremity of some solid conductor and never in midair as in the case of the Brown Mountain lights.

Some scientists have advanced the theory that the lights are a mirage. Through some peculiar atmospheric condition they believe the glowing balls are reflections from Hickory, Lenoir and other towns in the area. The only drawback to this theory is that the lights were clearly seen before the War between the States, long before electricity was used to produce light.

In recent years scientists have been more concerned about exploring outer space. Perhaps they have forgotten that there are mysteries on our own planet still unsolved. The Brown Mountain lights are one of them.

Alice of the Hermitage

She died more than a hundred years ago, but she still comes back to the home she loved

It was one of the most elaborate balls of the Charleston season. A few short years before the coming of the War for Southern Independence, there was no hint of wartime austerity. Richly attired young men bowed before lavishly gowned girls in the sumptuous private ballroom. And soft music played on into the early morning hours.

One young girl stood out among the rest, lovely as a perfect camellia. Her flowing white gown, trimmed with lace and exquisitely embroidered, floated about her as she went through the figures of each dance with graceful perfection. No one could have guessed that when next the girl wore this dress she would be in her coffin.

Student at an exclusive young ladies' school in Charleston, Alice had been a reigning belle for two seasons. Shortly after the ball she was stricken with a fever thought to be malaria. Since it was near the end of the school term the head mistress decided to send her to her home at Murrell's Inlet north of Georgetown with a returning neighbor.

By the time Alice reached "The Hermitage," the family summer home built by her father in 1849, her condition was critical. Her malady was not malaria but the deadly typhoid. In spite of the loving care of her family she died within a few days.

The beautiful ball gown was unpacked and the wan but still lovely young girl was dressed in it for the last time. She had worn this same dress when a famous painter did her portrait, a portrait which could be seen in "The Hermitage" until recent years.

The body was placed in a glassed-in casket in Alice's own room and all who saw her exclaimed over her beauty even in death. At the time her mother was many miles away visiting relatives. No decision could be made as to a final resting

181

place for the body so Alice was buried on the plantation. She was later removed to the church-yard and buried near relatives in the live-oak shaded cemetery.

It was not long after Alice's death that a Northern cousin arrived with her young son for a visit. The next morning at breakfast the boy asked who was the pretty lady in the white dress he had seen in his room. His mother told him that it had only been a dream. But the youngster steadfastly maintained that he had seen a girl who would not answer when he asked her name but only shook her head and smiled.

The hostess recognized his description as that of the girl who had died a few years before. A short time later Alice's apparition appeared in the garden to members of the family.

"The Hermitage" looks now much as it did at the time Alice lived there. For three genera-tions she has continued to appear. Sometimes she walks through the garden in the moonlight. And on other occasions she may be seen sitting in the window of the room which was once her own. All who have seen her have been amazed at the beauty of this lovely young apparition who still returns to the home she loved so well.

At dusk the low country near Georgetown where Alice walks is a place of haunting beauty.

The Night

the Spirits Called

**A ghostly plea for help added to the terrors of the
stormy night for the crew of the Cape Fear river boat**

Savage storms of sleet and snow are rare, indeed, in Wilmington, North Carolina. But
not long after the Civil War a Christmas season
came which was long remembered for its icy
gales and inclement weather.

Broken branches and signs were strewn everywhere along the deserted streets. Many of the
older buildings had been unroofed and torn by
the fierce winds. Each day brought news of ship-
wrecks along the coast from Hatteras to Cape
Fear. And every mail brought word of more lives
lost at sea.

But the Southport mail boat *Wilmington* made
her daily runs without a break, although there
were times when the gale winds would toss her
about until her upper rail was almost hidden by
foam.

On December 24th there were indications that
the weather would change. The *Wilmington* was

due to sail at 5 o'clock and long before the warning whistle blew, a group of passengers bound for
Southport boarded the boat with armloads of
Christmas parcels. But before the steamer could
leave the dock trouble had already begun. The
voyage could not be made until a kettle in the
engine room was mended. Captain Harper announced to his passengers that it would take at
least six hours to repair the damage.

As darkness came the wind and snow increased.
All the passengers but one decided to leave for
more comfortable quarters on shore. Not averse
to some sociability, the captain began to chat
with his lone passenger. And soon the stranger
began telling of Colonial times.

"My great-grandfather was William McMillan
of Edinburgh, who enlisted with the Camerons in
the Rebellion of '45 and after the battle of Cul-
loden was compelled to leave his country.

183

"He was a personal friend of Governor Gabriel Johnston of North Carolina. Johnston had invited him to come and make his home among the Cape Fear Scotsmen already settled in what is now Robeson county. On his way McMillan stopped at Waddell's Ferry where he became an ardent Whig sympathizer. Many of his countrymen were here at the Ferry and they had never forgiven the British oppression.

"Unfortunately, McMillan and the two Highland Scots who had been marked as doomed men were captured by the cruel Tory Colonel, David Fanning. The Scots were to be put to death for their so-called treason in violating the oath of allegiance to the British crown—an oath reluctantly given which bound them to a hostile sovereign.

Fanning marched his prisoners to the town of Brunswick, now a ruin on Orton Plantation. Then he consigned the three men to the dank dungeons of an old prison ship which was anchored in the bay opposite Sugar Loaf Hill.

"After several agonizing and fruitless efforts to escape its gloomy hold they were brought to shore, given a mock trial and sentenced by Fanning to immediate execution. The place of execution was near Brunswick. Here the two Highlanders were bound together to a large pine tree.

"A platoon of unwilling soldiers drew up before them and fired. Their quivering, bleeding bodies were then unbound from the tree which it is said still marks the spot where these martyrs to freedom died. Then McMillan was brought forward, held by guards, to meet the same fate. But, an exceptionally powerful man, he struck one of them senseless, broke away from the other and managed to escape into the woods. From there he made his way back to Robeson county.

"The Orton people hold an old tradition that on stormy nights ghosts of the two Scotsmen walk abroad. They have also been seen on their phantom boat in search of rescuers."

By now the moaning wind and crackling sleet conspired to chill the flow of conversation. Harper had begun to think of the dangerous run ahead of him through the storm. It was almost midnight. But repairs were completed and the boat pulled away from the dock. The night was so thick that even the river lights were obscured. At times the Captain slowly felt his way without a guiding mark while the mate, Peter Jorgenson, kept the lead line going constantly.

"Of all the nights I ever saw this is the worst," complained Harper. "The snow is coming down faster than ever and I'm afraid we're off course." At this moment the wheel refused to budge. "Here's worse luck still," he exclaimed, "the rudder chains are jammed!"

"We are out of the channel, sir!" shouted Jorgenson from the deck. "She shoals again!—two fathoms, one, a half one fathom. We've hit the lower jetty, sir!" And the ship went crashing over the rotted timbers of the old submerged pier which had not felt a keel in over seventy years.

The Captain swore. His Presbyterian passenger seemed to concur silently. The tide was low and Harper's efforts to twist the *Wilmington* free only seemed to make matters worse. There was nothing to do but wait for high tide to float her clear.

All hands but Peter Jorgenson sought the comfort of the furnace fires. The mate walked the upper deck restlessly, immersed in memories of the Christmas season in his own land. A sudden, icy gust of wind broke his reverie. As he turned in his pacing to and fro, he saw the dripping figure of a man leaning against the weather rail.

The hair and beard were flecked with snow and the face was distorted with suffering.

"How did you get here? What do you want?" cried Peter, going forward with his hand outstretched to grasp the man. There was no answer. The figure raised a bony arm and pointed out over the water looking like some weird scarecrow of the deep.

"Who are you? Are you mad?" shouted Peter. As he reached out to lay hold of the figure his fingers met nothing but air. Where a man had stood a moment before there was now just the falling snow and darkness.

A few minutes later when Peter reached the pilot house his face was ashen with fear. The Captain gave him an angry look and turning to McMillan said, "This man is drunk!"

"I am far from drunk," declared the mate. "I have not touched a drop. On my word, I have seen a ghost!"

"Now I know you're drunk!" exclaimed the Captain. "Who ever saw a ghost? McMillan, have you ever seen a ghost?"

"I do not doubt that Mr. Jorgenson has real reason for his alarm," replied McMillan. "I know of things in my experience beyond the realm of reason. But first let us search for Peter's ghost."

The Captain agreed and the crew was called up and ordered to search the ship. McMillan

joined the party and every corner was closely scrutinized by the light of safety lamps. There was nothing to be found. Each man was questioned and all denied having seen anything out of the ordinary.

"The night is dark and perhaps you were having a dream," said the Captain to Jorgenson.

"Does a man having a dream walk in the bitter cold with a lantern in his hand as I was doing then?" demanded Peter. "I stood within a yard of the stranger and I can never forget that fearful face. My lamp shown brightly and illuminated the figure clearly."

"Well, if ghosts are taking their walks tonight we may see troops of them before we get out of this confounded mess," said the Captain sarcastically. "How is the tide, Mr. Jorgenson?"

"It has been running up for quite two hours. She is already lifting a little, sir." In less than an hour more the steamer eased off the old jetty and was on her way again.

Suddenly, attracted by the wheel house lights, a blinded gull came crashing through the glass and fell dying at McMillan's feet.

"The foul fiend is certainly abroad tonight," cried the Scotsman, greatly shaken. "This is the worst of all bad omens."

But they had left the storm behind and the Captain was optimistic. Soon he began pointing out historic spots on the river shore as the lights of Kendal and Orton were safely passed.

"Eight years before the Boston Tea Party, of which so much is made, the minute men from Brunswick and Wilmington surrounded Tryon's Palace and demanded the surrender of the King's Commissioner. The Boston men disguised themselves as Indians. But Ashe and Waddell scorned such subterfuge and, seizing the British warship's

185

rowing barge, they placed it on wheels and carried it in a triumphal march to Wilmington."

He had barely gotten these words out of his mouth when he and the others heard human cries.

"It is some poor castaway," said the Captain. Reaching for the signal wire, he rang for a full stop. More desperate screams came from the water and brought McMillan from the wheel house with a look of terror on his face.

"On deck!" shouted the Captain.

"Aye, aye, sir!" came the answer from below.

Upon the troubled water, two cable lengths abeam, appeared a boat surrounded by a phosphorescent glow. It was an ancient rowing barge so foul with barnacles and slimy seaweed that Peter Jorgenson thought she must have been afloat a hundred years.

The Captain rubbed his eyes and looked again. "There's something uncanny about that thing. But it must be mortal men in trouble for spirits could not cry out with such anguish. Stand by and throw that barge a rope, Mr. Jorgenson."

The barge was soon just a cable length away. By now the horrified crew of the *Wilmington* beheld two gaunt human forms in tattered Highland dress from which emaciated legs emerged. Heavy chains extended from their ankles to their bloody wrists. As the barge with its grotesque occupants drew nearer McMillan saw their worn faces. Their hands were lifted beseechingly.

The Captain stood awe stricken at the sight. But suddenly, his voice trembling, he shouted to the mate, "Stand by and heave those men a line!"

Somehow, Peter made himself obey. At that moment the barge was lifted on a swelling wave which hurled it almost into his arms. Then as he heaved the rope across the rotten hulk, it and its shocking crew were gone!

The men of the *Wilmington* stood silent and appalled. Without a word the course was laid again. But the ship had hardly resumed her speed when the sound of more shrieks came from the darkness just ahead. The ship was put at half speed as Peter shouted, "Starboard, hard a-starboard, sir; we are running down a wreck!"

The Captain wrenched the helm to one side, narrowly avoiding collision with what proved to be a vessel bottom up. Clinging to it were two exhausted seamen. The crew of the *Wilmington* helped the wretched men aboard.

As Peter held his lantern to the face of one of the seamen who had fainted on the deck, he cupped both hands around his mouth and shouted excitedly to the Captain.

"This is the man! This is the ghost I saw when we ran aground."

The skipper and McMillan studied the seaman's face intently. It was just as Jorgenson had described the face of the ghost—the vanishing stranger.

"How could this be?" exclaimed the Captain.

"His spirit was abroad in search of help," replied McMillan. "I've read and heard of similar phenomena."

"But how do you explain the phantom of the barge?"

"I dinna ken, I dinna ken," answered McMillan, lapsing into the Highland manner of speech. He would say no more.

After the castaways were fed they told their story. Their schooner, bound from Nassau for a northern port, had been wrecked by the gale off the coast. All the crew must have perished save these two men. They had clung fast to the hulk of their boat which had miraculously drifted into the river with the tide.

When asked if either of them had seen the *Wilmington* before, the seaman whom Jorgenson recognized said he had been partly unconscious for a time and thought he saw a steamer coming to their aid. But he could not for a moment recall the encounter described by the mate.

The Captain's eyes met those of McMillan, then turned away.

A ghost town on the Cape Fear River, Brunswick was founded in 1726 and once was a leading port of North Carolina. It was occupied by the Spanish in 1748, and later, after being retaken by the British, it was the scene of resistance to the Stamp Act in 1766. In the picture are the ruins of St. Phillips church. The town is preserved as a historic site.

Swamp Girl

**A South Carolina couple picked up a young girl walking
beside the road, only to receive the shock of their lives**

Between the gloomy depths of the dank South Carolina swamp and the moonlit ribbon of highway walked the solitary figure of a girl. She wore a black hat and a black suit and in her hand she carried a traveling bag.

On each side of the road beyond the shoulder was a steep drop of perhaps twenty feet to a drainage ditch. From the swamp's watery blackness rose the incessant rasping cheep of thousands of small creatures. Live oaks with their ragged gray shrouds of Spanish moss whispered among themselves with each passing breeze.

It was along this lonely stretch of highway, through the swamp toward Columbia, South Carolina, that the headlights of the car discovered her.

The driver of the car was a man whom we shall call J. C. Tipton. An employee of the Land Bank, he and his wife were on their way to Columbia. They wondered what a nicely dressed

*It is along this lonely stretch of highway
that the Swamp Girl has been seen
hurrying to the bedside of her desperately
ill mother.*

girl was doing walking alone along the highway at this late hour and slowed to a stop to see if they could help her.

The girl thanked them. "Yes," she replied, "I am trying to get to Columbia to visit my mother, who is desperately ill." She then gave them the address of a house on Pickens Street. Since the car was a two door sedan the man's wife courteously held the back of her own seat to allow the girl to get in.

After the stranger was settled in the back, Mrs. Tipton closed the car door and for a few minutes she and her husband continued their conversation. Soon, however, Mrs. Tipton made a remark about the unseasonably hot weather, speaking over her shoulder to include the girl in the conversation. Hearing no answer she turned around to look in the back. Their passenger had vanished.

She peered down in the foot of the car but it, too, was empty. There was no possible way for anyone to get out of that car without the couple in the front seat knowing it.

189

Mrs. Tipton began to scream. Her husband, who was frightened too, almost ran off the road. Nothing he could say to his wife seemed to calm her. He was so concerned over her mounting hysteria that he drove to Columbia as quickly as possible and rushed his wife to a hospital. She was given sedatives to quiet her, and when the doctors told Tipton his wife was resting comfortably and would be all right, he remembered the number on Pickens Street.

He decided he would go there and find out what he could. It was quite late when he finally reached the house. Although it was completely dark he decided he would ring the bell. He had waited several minutes before there was a flicker of light in the hall and a sleepy looking young man opened the door.

"You needn't tell me what you came for," the man said. "You came to tell me you picked up a young lady in the swamp and she disappeared."

Tipton was so surprised he couldn't say a word. He simply nodded.

"That was my sister," added the young man sadly. "She was killed in an automobile wreck in the swamp three years ago while she was on her way to the hospital to see our mother. Two other people have had the same experience you have, each time on the anniversary of her death."

Moonlight illuminates the swamp beside the road where the girl appeared.

190